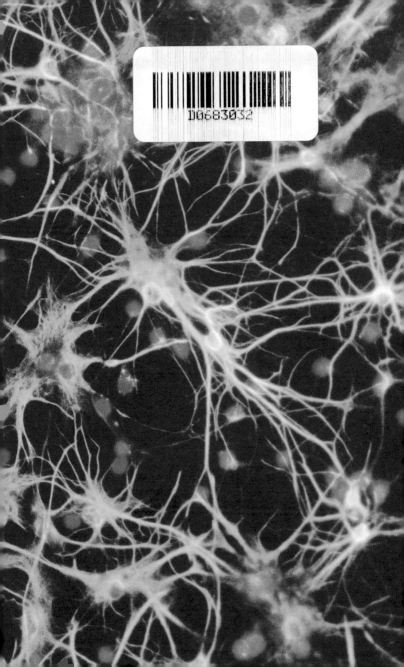

Freaky
Phenomena

Freaky
Phenomena

OVER 1,500 AMAZING AND BIZARRE FACTS

JOEL LEVY

This Modern Books edition published by Elwin Street Productions

Copyright © Elwin Street Limited 2007

Conceived and produced by
Elwin Street Limited
144 Liverpool Road
London N1 1LA
www.elwinstreet.com

Designer: Sharanjit Dhol

See page 144 for picture credits

ISBN-13: 978-0-9556421-5-9
ISBN-10: 0-9556421-5-9

Printed in China

Contents

1 The Unexplained 7

Tales of the peculiar and unexpected 8
Mystery monsters 9
Vampires 11
Werewolves 13
Zombies 13
Mediums and spiritualism 14
Lost civilisations 16
Magic and witchcraft 18
Super psychics 25
Wild talents 26
Supernatural saints 29
Mad myths and loco legends 30

2 Out there 33

What's out there? 34
The creation of the Universe 34
The weirdest stuff in the Universe 34
The Solar System 38
The end of the world as we know it? 42
The final frontier 44
Pigsty in space – space junk 45
Is anybody out there? 46
UFOs and alien abduction 48

3 Natural phenomena 55

Weird episodes in the natural world 56
Strange rains 56
Coloured snow 58
Mighty winds 58
The light fantastic 61
Wild weather – meteorological extremes 63
Mountain high, valley deep 67
Eruptions and quakes 68
Earth's strangest places 69
Singing sands, ringing rocks, and waterguns 72

CONTENTS

4 Bizarre animals and weird plants 73

Weird wildlife 74
Animal magic 74
Oldest organisms 79
Man-eaters and cold-blooded killers 79
Animal death matches 84
Amazing insects and astonishing arthropods 86
Poison plants 88
Psychic pets and intelligent animals 89

5 Being human 91

There's a freak in all of us 92
Bewildering body bits 92
Stupendous senses 96
Gross bodily fluids 99
Diseases 104
Sleeping and dreaming 106
Dream symbolism 107
Altered states of consciousness 108
Unusual mutations 110

6 Curious cultures 113

Trends of human societies 114
Amazing antiquity 114
Worst rulers in history 118
Medieval Torturers 120
Fashion frenzy 122
Strangest laws in the world 125
Strange festivals and holidays of the world 126

7 Freaky future 127

World of the future 128
Bizarre inventions 128
Futuristic foods 130
Things you can buy from vending machines 132
Robots 133
Transport of the future 135
Jetpack 137
Transporters 139

Index 140

THE
UNEXPLAINED

Tales of the peculiar and unexpected

Mankind has always been fascinated, awed and terrified in equal measure by what it does not understand or cannot explain: the supernatural (phenomena that seem to be outside or beyond the natural world, such as gods, ghosts and magic) and the paranormal (phenomena that might prove to be part of the natural world if we could investigate and understand them, such as psychic powers). Unexplained instances and abnormal events happen more often than one would expect.

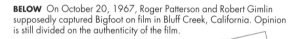

BELOW On October 20, 1967, Roger Patterson and Robert Gimlin supposedly captured Bigfoot on film in Bluff Creek, California. Opinion is still divided on the authenticity of the film.

Mystery monsters

Before the world was explored and its inhabitants categorised there was more room in the world for bizarre or unlikely creatures to exist – why should a unicorn seem any less plausible than a giant sea monster that blows water out of a hole in its back, to people who will never see either of them? Even today, however, mystery creatures lurk at the fringes of normal science. The science of cryptozoology, from the Greek for 'the study of strange animals', investigates everything from the Loch Ness Monster to Bigfoot. Following are the top five cryptozoological creatures most likely to exist.

Top five most likely cryptozoological creatures

1. **Bigfoot:** *Known by many names, such as 'yeti', 'sasquatch', and 'orang pendek', this creature is thought to be an ape man – a relative of* Homo sapiens *that survived extinction and lives on in wilderness areas.*

2. **Alien big cats:** *These aren't extraterrestrial kitties, but normal big cats in the wrong place, such as the British countryside. There are regular sightings of panther-like big cats and farmers regularly blame them for the loss of sheep.*

3. **Sea serpents:** *There have been reports of giant sea monsters throughout history, including quite recently such as the Monster Tadpole sighted off Australia's Great Barrier Reef in 1964. We know little about the deep ocean, where new species are discovered all the time.*

4. **Lake monsters:** *Sightings are reported from lakes all over the world and the most famous of all is Nessie – the Loch Ness Monster. No definite proof is ever found and many scientists think the lakes are too small to support large creatures.*

5. **Chupacabras:** *This term is Spanish for 'goatsucker' and refers to a monster seen throughout Latin America, described as a weird wolf-kangaroo hybrid with spines on its back, which sucks all the blood from goats and other livestock.*

Top five strangest cryptozoological creatures

These hybrid creatures that couldn't possibly exist, could they?

1. **Kappa:** *Japanese monster described as a monkey-turtle hybrid with the legs of a frog. A kappa has a pool of liquid in the top of its head, and is very fond of cucumbers.*

2. **Amemait:** *Ancient Egyptian monster with the body of a hippo, the tale and snout of a crocodile, and the head and mane of a lion.*

3. **Catoblepas:** *African monster with the body of a buffalo, the legs of a hippo, a long neck and the head of a warthog. Gives off a foul stench and is fatal to look at.*

4. **Manticore:** *A beast with the body and head of a lion, wings of a bat, tail of a scorpion and the face of a human. It entraps its victims with a friendly smile but can fire poisonous quills from its tail.*

5. **Bonnacon:** *Central Asian creature similar to a buffalo but with horns like a ram. Renowned for its ability to spray from its rear-end toxic discharges that can destroy whole regions.*

BELOW The Bonnacon, taken from *Bestiarius – Bestiary of Ann Walsh*, a collection of moralized fables about actual and mythical animals, generally believed to be of English origin, c. 1400–25. The creature was also described by Pliny in his work *Naturalis Historia*.

Vampires

Thanks to Bram Stoker and the countless celluloid adaptations of his tale, the vampire is probably the world's best known supernatural creature. Its literary antecedents, however, predate Stoker by nearly a century, stretching back to a gothic tale by Lord Byron in 1816; while in folklore the vampire dates back to ancient times and beyond.

Vampires feature in folklore from all around the world. In Portugal they are called *vampiro*, in India *vetala*, among Native North Americans *anchanchu*, in South America *azeman*, in Trinidad *sukuyan* and in Malaysia *bajang*.

According to folklore a vampire is created when any or all of the following takes place: a victim is bitten by another vampire; commits suicide; a black cat leaps over the open coffin of a victim; and/or uncovered mirrors are present at a dead person's wake.

RIGHT Vlad the Impaler, also known as Vlad Dracula, was the prince of Wallachia, now part of Romania, in the 15th century. He is best-known for the legends of exceedingly cruel punishments that he imposed during his reign and served as the inspiration for Bram Stoker's *Dracula*.

Traditional methods used to ward off vampires

Until relatively recently – the early 20th century – in some parts of Europe people lived in mortal fear of vampires as real and threatening entities. A body of folklore built up, detailing how to protect people, homes and the corpses of the newly dead from the depredations of the undead.

How to ward off vampires

Object	How it is used
Strings of garlic and garlic flowers	Hung around the home or person
Wild roses, wolfsbane (a herb), dog rose, hemlock and wormwood	Hung around the home or person
Crosses, holy water and other religious symbols	Kept about the person or fixed to doors and walls
Fierce dogs with large eyes painted on their foreheads	To guard one's home
Ash from cremated vampires	Fed to potential victims such as family members

FACT

The most haunted house in the world was said to be Borley Rectory, a large house in Essex, England. Over 200 sightings were said to have been reported there, including a phantom horse and coaches, and a ghostly nun, before it burned down in 1939. It is now thought that a lot (perhaps all) of the sightings and reports were either faked or never happened.

Werewolves

Shape-shifting creatures feature in the folklore of most cultures around the world and throughout history. In northern lands the wolf was often an object of such folklore. In the modern era, psychologists have described a delusional state called 'lycanthropy', where the patient believes he or she can literally transform into a wolf.

Identifying features of a werewolf

Folklore from all around the world is fairly consistent in its description of the physical characteristics of werewolves. Following are the agreed-upon identifying features:

- *Eyebrows meet in the middle*
- *Index fingers same length as middle fingers*
- *Hairy palms*
- *Red hair and blue eyes (from Greek folklore)*
- *Changes into horrible wolf creature at full moon*

Zombies

Zombies are the living dead – reanimated corpses brought back to life to serve a sorcerer (or, in the movies, to eat people's brains). The word originally comes from the voodoo religion of the Carribbean, and may derive from the West African words *nzambi*, 'god', or *zumbi*, 'flesh'.

Targets for becoming zombies are the weak and sick, and especially those with a mental illness. A zombie is created by feeding someone a sub-lethal dose of *coup de foudre*, a potion made from puffer-fish poison, tetrodotoxin. Once the victim falls into a near-death state, they are fed a powerful hallucinogen. Suggestion and brainwashing techniques are employed to make the victim believe they are dead and must serve their master. Zombies are kept under the influence of their master with regular doses of potions.

Mediums and spiritualism

A medium is someone who claims to be able to communicate with the spirits of the dead. Some mediums claim to channel the spirit, allowing the deceased to speak or write messages using the medium's body. Spiritualism, a religious movement whose adherents believed in the ability to communicate with the dead, florished from the 1840s until the 1920s and still exists in various forms today.

Top five most celebrated mediums

1. **The Fox Sisters:** *Kate (1838–92) and Maggie Fox (1836–93) started off the spiritualist movement when they claimed to be able to talk to a household ghost by interpreting the rapping sounds it made. They later confessed that they made the sounds themselves by popping their joints.*

2. **Daniel Dunglas Home (1833–86):** *A Scottish medium who could float, levitate objects, summon strange lights, handle red-hot coals and elongate his body. He was never proved to be a fraud.*

3. **Eusapia Palladino (1854–1918):** *An Italian medium who could apparently levitate, move heavy furniture and make her features appear in a sealed box of putty. She was caught faking several times.*

4. **Florence Cook (1856–1904):** *In 1871, as a 15-year old girl, Cook convinced noted scientist Sir William Crookes that she could materialise a spirit called Katie King. Crookes believed her, despite the fact that King looked a lot like Cook, who was allowed to perform the 'materialization' while hiding in a cupboard from which King would subsequently emerge.*

5. **Mina 'Margery' Crandon (1888–1941):** *An American medium who could materialise a 'teleplasmic hand' – a hand supposedly made from spirit matter. She used to perform in the nude and was exposed as a fraud by Harry Houdini.*

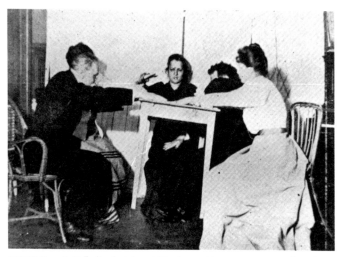

ABOVE Eusapia Palladino leviates a table observed by eminent scientists from the Society for Psychical Research in about 1890.

Ouija boards

These are boards that are used during séances. They have letters, numbers and simple words (such as 'yes' and 'no') marked on them. The idea is to use a pointer, like a computer mouse, which is guided by the spirits to point to letters and words that spell out the answers to questions. Sitters at a séance have to put their hands on the pointer. It probably works because their involuntary muscle twitches and movements guide it – this is known as the 'ideomotor effect'.

FACT

'Ectoplasm' refers to matter formed from energy from the spirit world allowing spirits to manifest in our world. Some mediums produced strange shapes and forms in ectoplasm, but it was usually just cheesecloth or wet muslin, swallowed and regurgitated.

Lost civilisations

Did civilisation really start in ancient Mesopotamia and Egypt in the 4th millennium BCE, or was there a much older, original super-civilisation from which all later civilisations sprang? The most common candidate for this lost civilisation is Atlantis, but did you know there were many other lost continents and civilisations?

Top three lost civilisations

1. **Atlantis:** *Famous continent that supposedly used to take up most of the Atlantic O cean but was destroyed by huge earthquakes and sank beneath the waves 9,000 years ago. The story comes from the ancient Greek philosopher Plato (427–347 BCE), but geologists now know that there is no sunken continent beneath the Atlantic. Perhaps Plato was referring to an ancient civilisation somewhere else – suggestions range from Antarctica and Ireland to Crete and Spain.*

2. **Lemuria:** *Hypothetical continent originally located in the Indian Ocean to explain the distribution of fossil lemurs (which are found from Pakistan to Malaysia, as well as in Madagascar). Later writers claimed it was in the Pacific, or that it existed before Atlantis and was home to earlier species of human.*

3. **Hyperborea:** *In Greek mythology this was a land in the far north where the Sun always shined. The Nazis and other fascists invented a ridiculous mythology of their own in which Hyperborea was the original home of super-humans who founded Atlantis. They claimed it was at the North Pole.*

FACT
In May 2001, sonar mapping discovered an undersea land plateau north of Bolivia, near Cuba, with apparent architectural edifices resembling pyramids and other structures such as roads and buildings. Researchers suggested that this might be Atlantis.

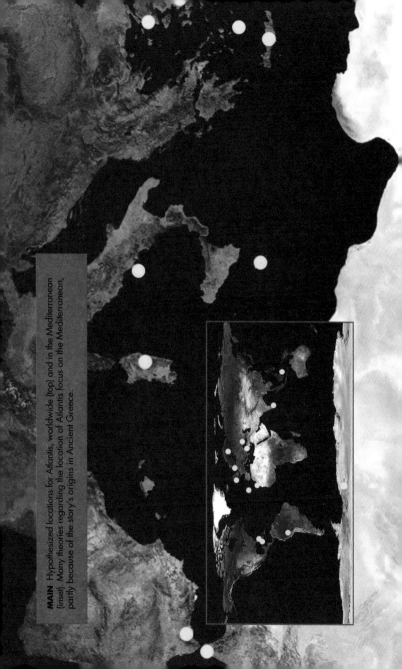

MAIN Hypothesized locations for Atlantis, worldwide (top) and in the Mediterranean (inset). Many theories regarding the location of Atlantis focus on the Mediterranean, partly because of the story's origins in Ancient Greece.

Magic and witchcraft

Many historians think that magic was simply what science used to be called, until science as we know it was 'invented' in the 17th century. There are still many people today who believe that magic is real. According to some sources, over three-quarters of the world's population still relies on herbal medicine, which is often used as part of magic, while even in the United States belief in astrology is maintained at a steady 30 per cent.

Some types of magic

Name of magic	What it means
Kabbalah	A system of Jewish magic based on medieval writings but recently adopted as a fashionable philosophy by many celebrities. Kabbalah comes from the Hebrew word for 'tradition'.
Divination	Foretelling the future. Divination can be performed in many ways – see page 19.
Necromancy	Raising the spirits of the dead for evil purposes, or possibly just for a chat.
Alchemy	Mixing of substances to try to turn lead into gold and find the elixir of life, which makes one immortal.
Wicca	Modern form of pagan witchcraft, using spells and rituals for the purposes of good.

FACT

The belief that a person can cause bad luck for someone else simply by looking at them is known as the 'evil eye'.

Some types of divination

Name	Objects used or examined
Augury	Bird behaviour – for example, swallows flying low means an early winter
Cartomancy	Cards such as Tarot cards
Ceromancy	Patterns made by molten wax dropped into water
Scrying (a type of crystallomancy)	A sphere of crystal or glass (i.e. a crystal ball)
Haruspicy	Animal entrails
Moleosophy	Moles on a person's body
Myomancy	Movements of mice
Numerology	Number values of letters in a name or word
Oenomancy	The patterns formed by pouring wine onto the ground or into a dish
Oneiromancy	Dreams
Phallomancy	Penis
Psychometry	'Emanations' or 'imprints' in the mind of an individual from an object or place
Pyromancy	Fire
Rhabdomancy	A wand or divining rod (i.e. a stick of some sort)
Scatoscopy	Human excrement
Sideromancy	The movement of straws placed on a red-hot iron
Stichomancy	Opening a book at random and interpreting the first passage read
Tasseography	Tea leaves

How to scry in a crystal ball

The best known method of scrying is with a crystal ball, but other mediums with a reflective surface, such as water, polished precious stones or mirrors, should work as well. Prepare a quiet, dimly lit room, and get comfortable, as your scrying session should last about 20 minutes. Relax and gaze into your crystal ball, which will serves as a focus for your attention, to clear your mind of all distracting thoughts. Have an idea of what it is you want to see – for example, the near future – and watch out for random images appearing in your crystal ball. Make a note of these images, or speak them aloud, as they appear whatever they are, even if they seem irrelevant. Then review them altogether to interpret the meanings of your visions.

How to read palms

There are three major palm lines.

◆ The heart line *at the top of the palm, represents matters of the heart, both physical and emotional: If the line starts directly underneath the index finger, then you are content with your love life; below the middle finger indicates a selfish and materialistic outlook.*

◆ The head line *starts under the index finger and runs across the palm, representing the mind and the way a person thinks: A curved, sloping line indicates creativity; while a short line shows a preference for physical achievements.*

◆ The life line *starts above the thumb and travels in an arc towards the wrist: It represents vitality and vigor, physical health and general well being (although it's not actually tied to the length of a person's life).If it is curvy, you have a lot of energy; short and shallow may indicate that you let others control your life for you.*

LEFT The heart line is at the top of the palm. The head line starts under the index finger and runs across the palm. The life line starts above the thumb and runs toward the wrist.

The two laws of magic

Most magic is performed according to rules and rituals. The most basic rules of all, which underlie almost all magical practice, are:

1. **The Law of Association:** *Objects or words that are or have been associated with other things have power over those things. For instance, your name or a lock of your hair have power over you because they are or were associated with you. This means that if a magician gets hold of some of your hair he can cast a spell on you by performing magic on the hair.*

2. **The Doctrine of Correspondences:** *There is a secret order of correspondences throughout nature, which links things that might not ordinarily seem to be linked. For instance, according to the Doctrine, there are correspondences between: the Sun; certain types of plant, such as sunflowers or vines; certain types of mineral, such as gold; the colour yellow; and even certain names, places, animals and birds. This means that by using, say, sunflowers in a magical ritual you can tap into the spiritual and magical power of the Sun.*

The Burning Times

Since prehistoric times people were sometimes suspected of causing misfortune to others by practising witchcraft, and they were often persecuted or killed as a result. In Dark Age Europe the authorities tried to put a stop to this, and educated people and the Church argued that there was no such thing as witchcraft. But popular belief lingered on and would flare up in times of conflict or hardship. One of the worst such periods was the Burning Times, a craze for witch-hunting that spread across Europe in the 16th and 17th centuries, during which as many as 40–60,000 men and women were executed for witchcraft.

BELOW An illustration depicts a woman being burned at the stake for the crime of engaging in witchcraft, circa 1692.

How a witch was unmasked

In the 1640s Matthew Hopkins, self-proclaimed Witch-finder General of East Anglia, in England, hunted down, accused and tortured hundreds of people for being witches. Following were the traditional methods used for unmasking a witch:

◆ **Trial by ordeal:** *This was an ancient form of justice, based on the belief that if you were innocent God would protect you. One version was ordeal by fire, where the accused person had to cover a certain amount of ground while holding a red-hot iron bar or walk over red-hot metal.*

◆ **Dunking:** *Related to trial by ordeal, dunking was where the accused was bound hand and foot and dropped into a river or pond. It was said that because witches had renounced baptism the water would not accept them and they would float. If they were innocent they would sink, but contrary to popular belief they would then be rescued.*

◆ **Peine forte et dure:** *French for 'strong and heavy punishment', this involved being crushed under a board onto which heavy stones were placed. It was used when a person refused to plead either guilty or innocent. The person being tortured would either make a plea or die.*

◆ **Torture:** *More generally, it was considered legal to obtain confessions through torture, which could include thumbscrews and hot pincers.*

◆ **Witches' marks:** *It was believed that the Devil branded witches as his own, leaving marks that could be spotted by an expert. These could be moles, birthmarks, scars, tattoos, extra nipples and extra toes or fingers.*

◆ **Pricking:** *It was believed that the marked part of a witch could not feel pain and would not bleed, so a witch-finder would prick the relevant part of the skin with a needle or knife to see if it hurt or bled. Some witch-finders used fake pins, which made it look like the pin was going in when in fact it was not.*

FACT

One medieval theory to explain why a dunked witch would not float was that witches deliberately ate foods that made them fart. The gas would build up their guts, making them lighter than air, so they could fly.

Spells

Witches, wizards, magicians, sorcerers and simple common people have used an infinite variety of spells to try to get something they want. Some spells involve complex ingredients and rituals; others simply involve saying a few words – an incantation.

Spells from history

Purpose of spell	Method
To turn yourself into a hare	Recite the following charm: 'I shall go into a hare, With sorrow and sych and meickle care; And I shall go in the Devil's name, Ay while I come home again'.
To find your true love	Soak one of your socks in rosewater, dry it out, and put it under your bed. Send out nightly thoughts about your true love for a month, and then burn a red candle at sunset while thinking more about the object of your affections. Repeat this for seven nights.
To attract someone you like	Pick a half red/half green apple when the Moon is three days past full. Breathe on the green side and rub it with a red cloth while reciting the verse: 'Fire sweet and fire red, warm the heart and turn the head'. Kiss the red half, and give it to the object of your desire. If he/she eats it he/she will fall under your spell.
To summon a fairy (this spell was supposedly used to summon a fairy called Margarett Barrance, but could be used for any fairy)	Steep a crystal in hen's blood for three weeks, then wash it with holy water. On a Wednesday, three hazel wands inscribed with the fairy's name should be buried under a hill where fairies are suspected to live, all the while chanting the fairy's name. The following Friday, dig them up and chant the name while facing east and holding the crystal.

Super psychics

The scientific study of psychic powers is called 'parapsychology'. Parapsychologists use laboratory studies and statistics to investigate whether people really can display psychic powers. Some parapsychologists claim to have proved that telepathy really exists.

Types of psychic power

Psychic power	What it means	Also known as
Telepathy	The ability to receive and sometimes communicate information between two minds without the use of normal senses	Mind-reading, mental radio, thought transference
Clairvoyance	The ability to perceive information about objects, places and events without the use of normal senses	Remote viewing, far sight, second sight (Celtic lore)
Precognition	The ability to perceive information about the future	
ESP (extra-sensory perception)	A general term that covers all of the above	
Telekinesis	The ability to exert physical force (e.g. moving things, bending spoons) using the mind. There are many different types of telekinesis, including teleportation (the ability to move people or things between two points without actually travelling through the intervening space) and fire-starting	psychokinesis

Wild talents

Some people seem to have strange powers or abilities that aren't quite psychic powers but are nonetheless inexplicable, not to mention often pretty impressive. These are sometimes called 'wild talents'.

Electric and magnetic people

There is evidence that some rare individuals appear to become electrically charged or otherwise acquire the ability to affect electrical equipment and cause electricity-related effects (such as giving off sparks, starting fires or being able to generate static electrical forces). Others seem to have related powers of magnetism, so that metallic things stick to them or they can stick to the ground. There are a number of historical cases of this strange phenomenon, although there are skeptics who argue that these effects are simply tricks and illusions.

1. **Liew Thow Lin, 'Mr Magnet':** *Since 2001 this 70-year-old Malaysian man has featured in several newspaper reports as being able to pull a car to an iron plate that is magnetically stuck to his stomach. He can also reportedly make irons and cutlery stick to his chest.*

FACT

In the 1970s and 80s, at the height of the Cold War, the United States developed a psychic spying program called 'Operation Stargate'. Learning of Soviet efforts to train psychics, they were terrified they might be left behind in a psychic arms race. Psychics were used for many different operations including trying to locate missing aircraft and specific people.

2. **Angélique Cottin, the 'Electric Girl':** *In 1846 this 14-year old French girl apparently began to generate extremely strong fields of static electricity that made furniture fly across the room and gave shocks to people standing nearby.*

3. **Lulu Hurst, the 'Georgia Wonder':** *From 1883–5 Lulu Hurst appeared on stage as the 'Georgia Wonder'. Her act was to remain apparently glued to the spot, so that even the strongest man could not lift her.*

4. **The Tenkaev family:** *In the late 1980s a Russian man, Leonid Tenkaev, his wife, daughter and grandson all claimed to have acquired the mysterious power to make metal objects stick to their bodies. Leonid could make up to 23.6 kg (52 lbs) of metal stick to him.*

5. **Jennie Moran:** *In 1895 this 14-year old girl from Missouri started giving off sparks and generating a charge powerful enough to knock out anyone who shook hands with her. She killed her pet cat simply by picking it up.*

X-ray vision

Some people claim to be able to see through solid objects, such as blindfolds, while others claim to be able to see or at least 'visualise' the inside of a human body, allowing them to diagnose illnesses. Again, skeptics put these abilities down to trickery, stage magic and fraud:

1. **Kuda Bux:** *An Indian showman who toured the world in the 1930s and 40s, astonishing all with his ability to see through a blindfold. He could walk along a high ledge, ride a bicycle through traffic and read a newspaper, despite having his eyes taped shut, strips of black cloth tied around his head and a heavy bag over his head.*

2. **Natasha Demkina:** *This Russian teenager claims to have been able to see into people since 1998, allowing her to diagnose all manner of disease and illness. It is claimed that she is never wrong, although British scientists who tested her were not impressed.*

Fireproof people

Fire walking, where people walk over hot coals or embers in bare feet, can apparently be done by almost anyone. Scientists claim it can be explained through something called the 'Leidenfrost effect', which is where any moisture on the feet is heated into an insulating layer of vapor that protects the skin. But some people seem to have been more immune to heat than can be explained by any scientist. Here are four historical examples:

1. Josephine Giraldelli, the 'Original Salamander':
In the early 1800s she astonished audiences by being able to put her arm into a fire and stand barefoot on a red-hot shovel. Her stage name came from the folkloric idea that salamanders lived in fires and were immune to the flames.

2. Richardson: *An Englishman known throughout late seventeenth-century Europe, Richardson could put hot coals on his tongue and then chew them, could eat melted glass, and could handle red-hot iron and bend it with his teeth.*

3. Nathan Coker: *A blacksmith from Maryland, who in 1871 was reported to be able to put a white-hot shovel to his bare feet without injury, to swill molten lead in his mouth, and pick a red-hot iron out of the fire.*

4. Marie Sonet, the "Human Salamander": *In Paris in the 1750s this woman would put her feet into raging fire until her shoes and stockings were burned away, while her feet remained unharmed.*

ABOVE Walking on fire is now not considered such a feat, but more a company team-building exercise.

Supernatural saints

Weird things have happened to many Christian saints, including powers that would be described as psychic or supernatural if they happened today. Here are five saints with peculiar powers:

1. **St. Francis of Assisi:** *Something of a superman, St. Francis could talk to animals, levitate, glow and manifest stigmata (wounds that match those inflicted on Christ at the crucifixion; such as holes in the hands and feet from the nails, or marks on the head from the crown of thorns).*

2. **St. Joseph of Cupertino:** *Joseph could fly at will, swooping around the church and landing on the altar. Once he flew into an olive tree and perched on a branch for half an hour. He is recognised as the patron saint of air travellers such as pilots amd paratroopers.*

3. **St. Isidore:** *Despite dying in 1130 and initially being buried without even a coffin, Isidore's body did not decay and remained in near-perfect condition for 800 years, giving off a heavenly odor after 500 years.*

4. **Padre Pio:** *An Italian priest who died in 1968 and has recently been canonised, Padre Pio was a famous stigmatic, supposed to have experienced the pain of the crown of thorns and the scourging, and who was also, allegedly, able to bilocate (be in two places at once).*

5. **St. Angiolo Paoli:** *A 17th–18th-century Roman who was able to produce miraculous provisions – food from thin air – which he would give to the poor. On one occasion, during a severe drought, he miraculously supplied a picnic with salad, a tart, a basket of strawberries and a dessert.*

FACT
In Europe in the Middle Ages it was believed that there were over 7 million demons in the air, which could be inhaled or swallowed and would cause disease or make a corpse turn into a vampire.

Mad myths and loco legends

Cultures from all over the world and throughout history have told myths and legends about their ancestors, gods, and demons. Some of them are strange; others involve ingenious cruelty. Hades was the name for the underworld in Greek myth – the place where the dead went. Within Hades was a terrible pit called Tartarus, where the worst sinners or the most dangerous enemies of the gods were condemned.

Punishments in Hades

Character	Punishment
Sisyphus	Condemned to push a boulder up a hill for all eternity. Every time he got to the top it would roll down the other side and he would have to start again.
Ixion	Chained to a revolving wheel of fire for all eternity.
Tantalus	Condemned to spend eternity in a state of desperate thirst and hunger, standing up to his neck in a pool of refreshing water and with delicious grapes or figs dangling over his head. When he tried to take a mouthful of either, they would retreat just beyond his reach.
Tityus	Condemned to have his liver continually pecked by a pair of vultures.
The Danaïdes, the 49 daughters of Danaüs, King of Argos	Had to spend eternity trying to draw water from a well with leaky buckets.
Pirithous, companion of Theseus	Trapped forever in a chair of stone, held fast by snakes coiled around his feet or because the chair itself had melded with his flesh.

Gods and other divine beings in strange forms

God/goddess	Mythology	Description
Hathor	Egyptian	Goddess of motherhood. Sometimes depicted as having the body of a woman but the head of a cow or hippo
Xolotl	Aztec	God of lightning. Described as either a dog-headed man or a strange monster with backwards feet
Ganesha	Hindu	Body of a man, with a big belly and four arms; head of an elephant; red or gold all over
The Hecantonchires	Greek	Giants who each had 100 hands and 50 heads. They could throw rocks as big as mountains
Cherubim	Jewish and Christian	A group of angels who each have four faces – that of a lion, an ox, an eagle, and a man – the torso and hands of a man, hooved feet like a calf, and two pairs of wings
Rainbow Serpent	Australian Aboriginal	Giant multi-colored snake, responsible for water, rivers, and rainfall, among other things
Yum Cimil	Mayan	God of death. He was a skeleton who wore jewelry made of bones and was covered in black spots where his bones were decomposing
Nuwa and Fuxi	Chinese	Said to have created mankind. They had the heads, arms, and torsos of humans but the tails of snakes

Creation myths

Nearly every culture has a creation myth that explains how the wonders of the earth came to be.

People	Theory
Ainu (northern Japan)	The Earth was originally an ocean resting on the backbone of a giant trout, until the creator god sent a bird to create land and all the animals came down from heaven to live in the new world.
Australian Aborigines	The Universe was created during a period known as the Dreaming, when the gods and spirits awoke and traveled in a formless landscape, creating landmarks, features, plants, animals, and humans.
Some Chinese Taoist monks	The Universe was created from a giant egg, which contained a creator god called Pangu. After 18,000 years he hatched and separated the shell of the egg into two halves – one was the Heavens, the other the Earth – which took another 18,000 years. After this, Pangu rested and the parts of his body became the features of the Universe – for example, his facial hair became the stars and the Milky Way.
Ancient Greece	According to the writer Hesiod the ancient Greeks believed that Chaos had existed first, before giving birth to Gaia, the Earth. Gaia in turn gave birth to Uranus, the Heavens, and the two of them produced the Titans, among whom was Cronos, who castrated his father and separated the Earth and the Heavens.
Iriqouis (Native American tribe)	The Earth was created when a woman was banished from Sky World and needed a place to land. She got the animals to create the Earth for her by spreading mud and earth on the shell of a turtle, which still carries it around.
Mandinka (southern Mali)	The Earth was created when the creator god caused several sets of twins to grow in a cosmic womb. One of the twins took a piece of placenta and cast it out of the Heavens and it became the Earth.
Norse	Odin and his brothers created the Universe from the body of a giant called Ymir, and in particular used his eyebrows to create Midgard, or Earth.

OUT THERE

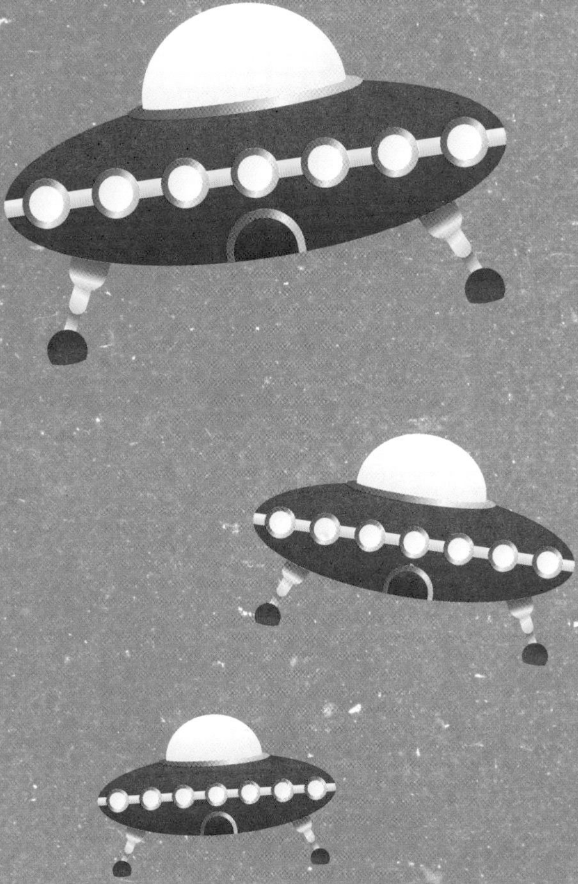

What's out there?

Mankind has always been fascinated by the skies, from the astronomers of early civilisations such as the Ancient Mesopotamians to modern day UFO spotters. There are plenty of strange goings on in the never-ending expanses of the Universe; invisible galaxies, the Solar System, theories for the creation, and possible destruction, of the Universe. What do we see when we look up at the night sky, and are we all alone in the Universe?

The creation of the Universe

The most popular scientific model for the creation of the Universe is currently the Big Bang theory. It states that time, matter, and energy were created in an enormous explosion about 13 billion years ago, which took just 10^{-4} seconds to create matter, although the first atoms took another 500,000 years to form. Sounds strange enough. This is not, however, the only theory about how the Universe was created. Here are some of the more interesting alternative views.

The weirdest stuff in the Universe

Anyone who thinks that there are no mysteries left for science to solve need look no further than the field of astronomy. Despite the massive leaps in our knowledge of

FACT
A millionth of a trillionth of a trillionth of a second after the Big Bang the temperature of the Universe was a whopping 100,000 billion billion billion°C.

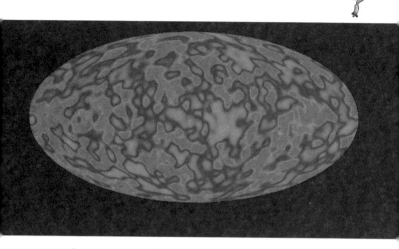

ABOVE Cosmic wave image of the Milky Way, showing remnants of the Big Bang.

the cosmos, there are still many things that astronomers do not know or cannot explain properly. For instance, astronomers know that the Universe must contain more matter then they can see with their telescopes. They call this invisible stuff 'dark matter'.

Invisible galaxies

In February 2005 astronomers announced that they had discovered the first of what they think are many invisible galaxies in the Universe. VIRGOHI21 is located within a cluster of galaxies in the constellation Virgo and is believed to be composed mainly of dark matter. It cannot be seen directly, but can be detected because of its influence on things around it.

Neutron stars

These are stars made entirely of neutrons, a type of subatomic particle, formed from the collapse of a massive star.

Although only about 20 km (12.5 miles) across,
a neutron star weighs half again as much as our Sun. This
means that on Earth one teaspoonful of neutron star would
weigh more than a billion tons.

Gravity

Gravity is the force that endows objects with weight. The
planets of our Solar System all have a different gravitational
pull from that of Earth, related to their own mass. So your
weight on another planet would be different from your
weight on Earth .

How much would I weigh on. . .

Planet	Relative Mass (Earth = 1)	Resulting Weight
Mercury	0.06	24 kg (52 lb)
Venus	0.82	57 kg (126 lb)
Earth	1.0	64 kg (140 lb)
The Moon	0.01	10 kg (23 lb)
Mars	0.11	24 kg (52 lb)
Jupiter	317.83	150 kg (330 lb)
Saturn	95.16	58 kg (128 lb)
Uranus	14.53	56 kg (124 lb)
Neptune	17.14	71 kg (157 lb)
Pluto	0.0021	4 kg (9 lb)

Gravity and Black Holes:

A black hole is the ultimate triumph of gravity over matter. It is a region of space where the gravitational field is so strong that not even light can escape. Black holes are formed from massive stars that run out of fuel, causing gravitational collapse as all the matter of the star's core is crushed to an infinitely small point, called a singularity.

Greedy stars and galactic pinball

Sometimes astronomers catch celestial objects such as stars and black holes in the act of 'swallowing' other ones.

Galactic cannibalism

When	Event
January 2002	The star V838 Monocerotis temporarily became the brightest star in the Milky Way after swallowing three planets in rapid succession. The extra material caused the star to explode into a massive red giant.
February 2004	Astronomers observed a star that had been knocked off course by an encounter with another star, veering too close to a black hole lurking in the center of galaxy RX J1242-11, which ripped it apart and swallowed some of it, emitting a giant 'burp' of X-rays – one of the fiercest outpourings of energy ever observed.

FACT

The human eye can see only about 3,000 stars on the clearest night, even though there are more than 100,000,000,000,000 stars in our galaxy alone.

The Solar System

There are nine planets in our Solar System, although the discovery of an object larger than Pluto, popularly called Xena, orbiting at much the same distance, has made people wonder if we should say there are ten, or only eight.

Relative sizes

If the Earth were the size of a grape, the Moon would be about 0.3 m (1 ft) away. The Sun would be about 1.8 m (6 ft) across, Jupiter would be the size of a melon, Saturn an orange, Uranus and Neptune the size of lemons, and Pluto would be almost too small to see. You would be the size of an atom.

Planet spotting

Mercury, Venus, Mars, Jupiter and Saturn can be seen with the naked eye, if you know where and when to look, which is how they were discovered by ancient civilisations. For example, Venus is always the third brightest object in the sky after the Sun and Moon and is known alternately as the Morning or Evening Star. Venus can also be seen by looking in the direction of the setting or rising sun, and it is visible for much longer periods of time than Mercury.

FACT

The Moon's gravitational pull is slowing the Earth's rotation by 2 milliseconds per century so that the day is becoming longer. Nine hundred million years ago a year was made up of 481 x 18-hour days rather than 365 x 24-hour days.

BELOW Diagram showing the relative sizes of the nine planets in our Solar System, which are all dwarfed by the size of the Sun.

Sun

Mercury

Venus

Earth

Mars

Jupiter

Saturn

Uranus

Neptune

Pluto

Peculiar planets

Each of the planets is eccentric or unusual in its own way. Here are some strange facts about each of the planets.

Mercury

Because of its strange orbit around the Sun, if you were standing on the surface of Mercury you would see the Sun get larger as it moved across the sky, stop moving, briefly reverse course, stop again, and then carry on while getting smaller.

Venus

Venus is the hottest place in the Solar System, with temperatures of 470°C (878°F – hot enough to melt lead) and pressures 90 times higher than on Earth.

Earth

If you stand at the Equator, you are spinning around the center of the Earth at about 1,600 km/h (1,000 mph), while also hurtling through space at 108,000 km/h (6,000 mph) as the Earth orbits the Sun.

Mars

Tiny tornadoes known as 'dust devils' are common on the surface of Mars. These whirlwinds are thought to be responsible for cleaning the dust off the solar panels that power the Mars Rover robots. Like a Martian carwash, this allows the robots to operate for far longer than originally expected.

Jupiter

Jupiter is mostly gas but its core is a rocky sphere about 10–15 times more massive than the Earth, where the temperature is 20,000°C (36,000°F).

Saturn

Saturn is most famous for its rings, made up of particles of ice and rock. The rings are about 270,000 km (168,000 miles) in diameter but only a few miles thick. If compressed, the material would form a ball less than 100 km (62 miles) across.

Uranus

Uranus is the only known planet that rotates on its side, south to north. Its equator is almost at right angles to the planet's orbit around the sun.It is possible that it was hit by a large object billions of years ago that tilted the planet on its side.

Neptune

Neptune has the strongest winds in the Solar System – up to 2,000 km/h (1,243 mph), which cause storm clouds to move at record speed. One atmospheric feature called the 'Scooter' travels round the planet every 16 hours.

Pluto

Due to the path of its orbit round the sun, for 20 years of its 248-year journey Pluto is closer to the Sun than Neptune.

The end of the world as we know it?

There are several geological and cosmological calamities that could spell doom for civilisation, and possibly even for all life on Earth: they are known as Extinction Level Events (ELE). Here is a rundown of the five most likely doomsday scenarios for the Earth:

1. **Super-volcano:** *At least a hundred times more powerful than any eruption within living memory, a super-volcanic eruption could strike anywhere at any time, with very little warning, and there's nothing we could do about it. It would pump so much dust and poisonous gas into the atmosphere that most sunlight would be shut out for years. The last time this happened – roughly 74,000 years ago – only 10,000 humans survived.*

ABOVE Artists at NASA have postulated that this is what an asteroid impact would look like, if an asteroid was to collide with a planet.

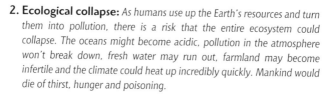

2. Ecological collapse: *As humans use up the Earth's resources and turn them into pollution, there is a risk that the entire ecosystem could collapse. The oceans might become acidic, pollution in the atmosphere won't break down, fresh water may run out, farmland may become infertile and the climate could heat up incredibly quickly. Mankind would die of thirst, hunger and poisoning.*

3. Gamma-ray burst: *When two celestial objects, such as a neutron star and a black hole, collide, they give off a huge burst of dangerous radiation called gamma rays. If a gamma-ray burst happened within 6,000 light years of Earth, it could irradiate the planet, boil away the atmosphere and fry every living thing on the planet like a cosmic microwave oven.*

4. Comet collision: *Comets are massive balls of ice and rock that hurtle through the Solar System at enormous speeds. If one was discovered on a collision course with Earth it would be almost impossible to stop, divert, or destroy, and could annihilate the entire planet. When the comet Shoemaker-Levy 9 crashed into Jupiter in 1994 it released more energy than the entire nuclear arsenal of Earth multiplied 750 times over, and left a scar the size of Earth. If this happened on Earth there would not be much left.*

5. Meteor mash-up: *A meteor is an asteroid (a big chunk of space rock) that hits the Earth. Earth is hit by 6 tons of meteorites a day, but they are all small enough to burn up in the atmosphere. Once every 10,000 years or so an asteroid big enough to wipe out a whole country hits the planet. An asteroid about 10 km (6 miles) across – big enough to cause an ELE – hits every 50–100 million years. Given enough warning, however, it is possible that mankind could work out a way to divert or destroy it.*

FACT

There is a risk that mankind's thirst for knowledge could destroy itself. Known as the 'Frankenstein Effect', our scientific and technological advances could very well prove fatal. Risk areas include nanotechnology, plagues, and electromagnetic pollution.

The final frontier

It's impossible to draw a definitive dividing line between the atmosphere and outer space – the further above the surface of the Earth you get, the thinner the atmosphere becomes, but even 1,600 km up there are still a few molecules.

The definition used by space agencies is the **Karman line**, named for Theodore Von Karman, who worked out that above 100 km (62.1 miles) altitude a craft needs so much thrust to stay aloft that it is effectively in freefall. Only around 450 people have been above this line (the number increases with each space mission).

Astronaut grooming and hygiene

Shuttle astronauts take a personal grooming kit that includes a hairbrush, comb, razor, shaving cream, toothbrush, toothpaste and nail clippers (although nails grow slowly in weightless conditions and a hairbrush wouldn't be much use).

When they are space walking, astronauts wear spacesuits fitted with diapers. On the spacecraft, because of weightlessness, toilets have foot loops and thigh restraints so that astronauts do not float away when using it. The toilets rely on a vacuum pump that sucks away the waste.

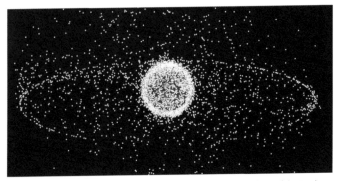

ABOVE Computer generated image of orbital debris being traked round the Earth.

Pigsty in space – space junk

A survey by the giant Arecibo radio telescope suggests that there are at least 150,000 objects larger than 1 cm (0.4 in) in orbit around Earth, and 1 million objects of 2 mm (0.08 in) or more. To a space-walking astronaut, however, even something smaller than this could be fatal: The front window of a space shuttle was chipped by an orbiting fleck of paint, and there may be tens of billions of such particles orbiting the Earth.

Manmade objects to leave the Solar System

Title	Launch Date	Destination	Original Mission
Pioneer 11	April 6, 1973	Constellation Aquila	Gather data on Jupiter, Saturn and interplanetary space
Voyager 1	September 5, 1977	Constellation Camelopardis	Gather data on Jupiter, Saturn and their moons; study edge of Solar System
Voyager 2	August 20, 1977	Interstellar space	Gather data on Jupiter, Saturn, Uranus, Neptune and their moons; study edge of Solar System

FACT
Because there is no atmosphere on the Moon, Neil Armstrong's first footsteps will not blow away. They are preserved in the dust that covers the Moon's surface and will remain there until someone – or something – erases them.

Is anybody out there?

Advances in science and technology have put us ever closer to getting in touch with our neighbours – if they exist . . .

Messages to outer space

The Voyager probe carries sounds and images that represent life on planet Earth. Some of the contents include:

◆ *Natural sounds, such as surf, thunder and wind; animal sounds; and manmade sounds*
◆ *Greetings in 55 different languages*
◆ *Musical tracks including Bach's Brandenburg Concerto, Chuck Berry's Johnny B. Goode and Louis Armstrong's Melancholy Blues*
◆ *Images including people watching TV and playing basketball*

ABOVE Is there life beyond what we know? Messages sent to outerspace may take up to 50,000 years to get a response.

FACT
The first rock music taken into space is thought to be a Pink Floyd tape taken to the space station Mir in 1988 by French astronaut Jean-Loup Chretien. Perhaps it was *Dark Side of the Moon.*

Most likely locations to support life

Planet	Reasons it might support life
Mars	Recent discoveries show that liquid water almost definitely flowed over much of the surface of the planet at one time, and that lots of frozen water still exists just below the surface and at the poles. Fossils of bacteria or other life forms may exist all over the planet, while liquid water, which could support life, might exist deep below the surface. Deep within Earth's crust bacteria thrive in similar conditions.
Europa (one of Jupiter's moons)	Beneath a thick, icy crust, a combination of magnetic activity and strong tides (caused by Jupiter's massive gravitational pull) may produce enough heat to keep water liquid. Conditions would be extreme, but possibly comparable with those around Earth's mid-ocean vents, which are teeming with life.
Titan (largest of Saturn's moons)	It has a smoglike atmosphere rich in chemicals similar to the atmosphere thought to have existed in Earth's early history, and also has water ice and a hot core. Some scientists think that it may already be home to bacteria blasted off the surface of the Earth by meteorite impacts.
Enceladus (small Saturn moon)	Tidal forces generate heat that seems to keep oceans of water in a liquid state just below the icy surface, occasionally driving huge geysers to spout into space. Heat and water could well equal life.

Alien visitation?

An astronomer has suggested that it wouldn't be hard to know if an alien civilisation has visited Earth. It would be fairly obvious, he maintains, because they would have left loads of space junk behind.

In May 2006, astronomer Ian Crawford postulated that the Moon would be the best place to look for proof of intelligent ETs (extraterrestrials) because anything they had left behind there would be in pristine condition.

UFOs and alien abduction

A UFO is technically anything that you see in the sky and cannot identify.

A spotter's guide to UFOs

UFOs first became popular in the late 1940s, but since then sightings have been traced back to the 19th century. Certain types of UFO seem to be the most common.

1. Airships: *In the 19th century people reported seeing UFOs shaped like airships (which we could call dirigibles or Zeppelins today).*

2. Saucers: *The classic UFO looks like a giant plate or saucer – a disc shape, sometimes with a dome in the middle.*

3. Crescents: *The 1947 sighting that started the UFO craze involved UFOs that looked like crescents.*

4. Cigars: *A commonly reported UFO shape is the cigar – a long cylinder with blunt, rounded ends. Perhaps these are related to the airship sightings of the 19th century.*

5. Triangles: *An increasingly common shape reported is the triangular UFO, often described as a black triangle with lights on the underside.*

Top five UFO hotspots

1. Marfa: *The town of Marfa in West Texas is famous for the Marfa Lights, where on a clear night strange lights are visible in the sky above the desert to the southwest.*

2. Hessdale: *A small valley in central Norway, 120 km (75 miles) south of Trondheim, where strange lights have frequently been observed.*

3. Gulf Breeze: *A city in Florida where many UFOs have been spotted.*

4. Warminster: *A town in Wiltshire, in the west of England, was the centre of a major UFO flap in the 60s and 70s. UFOs are still seen in the area.*

5. Nullabor Plain: *A desert in southern Australia, and the site of many strange UFO sightings and encounters.*

Rumored contents of Area 51

Area 51 is the popular name for a tract of land north of Nevada, Las Vegas, which houses Groom Lake Base, a secret airforce testing facility. It is also next to the test site of the original atomic bomb. Top-secret aviation projects have been developed there, including the U2 spy plane and the F-117A Stealth Fighter. The airspace around Area 51 is off-limits to local pilots, who call it 'Dreamland'.

For many UFOlogists (people who study UFOs), Groom Lake is also the centre of a massive web of conspiracy involving the United States Government and flying saucers. In particular it is claimed that scientists are 'reverse engineering' advanced technologies from UFOs that have crashed and been recovered (such as at Roswell).

Rumored contents include:

◆ *New top-secret military projects – for example, unmanned flying robot 'drones', stealth helicopters, and high-speed 'Aurora' planes*

ABOVE This sign is near Rachel, the closest town to the top secret base Area 51, Groom Lake, Nervada.

- *Intact and damaged alien spacecraft as well as spacecraft debris*
- *UFO-research and engineering workshops*
- *Dead aliens from crashed spacecraft. Government scientists are said to perform autopsies on them*
- *Live aliens who are being used in experiments*
- *Secret colonies of aliens*
- *An underground UFO base*
- *A biotechnological facility where humans and aliens work together to develop biological weapons (often passed off as natural diseases) and engineer alien–human hybrids*
- *The headquarters of a secret world government conspiracy, probably involving aliens*

Despite all of these various wild claims that exist about the secret base, there is absolutely no hard evidence to back up any of them.

The Close Encounters scale

The Close Encounters (CE) scale is part of a system of classification for UFO sightings and encounters proposed by leading UFO expert J. Allen Hynek in 1972. His original scale only went up to CE3. CE4 and 5 are recent additions, but these are not universally accepted by UFO researchers.

CE rating	What it means
CE1	Seeing objects or very brilliant lights from less than 457 m (500 yards).
CE2	UFO physically affects the environment, leaving traces of its presence such as sunburnt witnesses or marks from landing gear.
CE3	Witness sees/meets the occupants of the craft.
CE4	Witness goes into the spaceship (usually against his or her will).
CE5	Encounter involves paranormal elements, such as telepathy or poltergeist phenomena.

Top five explanations for UFOs

It is suspected that identified sightings are generally due to misidentifications, with hoaxes and psychological aberrations also accounting for a few percent of all cases. But there are also many cases that remain unexplained.

1. **Extraterrestrial hypothesis:** *This is the technical term for the belief that UFOs are spacecraft piloted by beings from other worlds.*

2. **Black projects:** *UFOs are highly advanced, top-secret military research craft. According to this theory, the military promotes the extraterrestrial hypothesis as a cover for the real nature of UFOs.*

3. **Earthlights:** *UFOs are balls of light created by natural but unknown geological and/or meteorological forces, such as stresses in the Earth's crust or a build-up of electricity in the air. These in turn create balls of charged gas that give off light and move around.*

4. **Life forms:** *UFOs are new and unknown forms of life – either entirely natural creatures that usually live in the upper reaches of the atmosphere, or semi-magical energy beings from other dimensions that appear to us in UFO form.*

5. **Misidentification:** *Even the keenest UFO nuts admit that 9 out of 10 UFOs have entirely normal explanations, and are simply the result of misidentifications. Common culprits are: stars and planets, normal aircraft, vehicle lights, ground-based lasers or spotlights, birds, hallucinations and dreams.*

✱ FACT

According to a 1991 survey of Americans, 2 per cent reported experiences that indicated they might have been abducted. This would mean that 1 in 50 Americans had been abducted – that's over 5 million, at the rate of 2,740 per day! Skeptics point out that this would mean the skies over America must be full of hundreds of alien spaceships every night.

ABOVE Depiction of a UFO over Roswell, New Mexico.

Major UFO sightings

According to some estimates, over 100,000 people have reported seeing an unidentified flying object since 1947.

Sighting	When	What happened
The Kenneth Arnold Sighting	June 1947	While flying near the Cascade Mountains of Washington State, in the northwest of the United States, private pilot Kenneth Arnold reported seeing a 'chain of nine peculiar-looking aircraft'. He didn't actually call them 'flying saucers', but said that they moved like 'saucers skipping over water'. An anonymous headline writer later turned this into the phrase 'flying saucers'.
Roswell	July 1947	The military issued an official press release saying that a flying saucer had crashed near Roswell, New Mexico, but later retracted the report and blamed a downed weather balloon. In the 1980s UFO researchers claimed to have spoken to witnesses who said the original story was the right one.
The First Abduction	September 1961	Betty and Barney Hill from New Hampshire reported a close encounter with a saucer-shaped UFO, but remembered few specific details until, under hypnosis, they revealed a tale of abduction and probing. Although not the first reported alien abduction, it was the first case to become widely known.
The Valentich Incident	October 1978	Australian pilot Frederich Valentich disappeared over Bass Strait between Tasmania and the mainland, after reporting an encounter with a UFO. No trace of him has ever been found.
Rendlesham Forest	December 1980	Strange lights were seen near USAF base in Rendlesham Forest, in Suffolk, England. Airmen who went into the forest to investigate claimed to have had close encounters. This case is often known as the British Roswell.

Abduction 101

Alien abduction is where a person believes he or she has been kidnapped by aliens, usually in order to be taken aboard a spaceship. Abduction experiences are almost certainly the result of a combination of dreams, hallucinations and false memories created through hypnosis. The vast majority of abduction experiences follow the same pattern.

1. *At night, usually while the abductee is in bed, he or she senses a strange presence, is paralysed, and feels a sense of unreality.*
2. *The abductee is taken aboard a spaceship, somehow floating out of bed and passing through walls and doors. A beam of bright light may be involved.*
3. *The abductee finds him- or herself on a slab, bed or table, with aliens examining and probing. The aliens may experiment on the abductee and implant and/or extract things.*
4. *The abductee may communicate with the aliens, be shown around the ship, and even been taken to another world.*
5. *The abductee wakes up back in bed, often with no memory of the abduction.*

NATURAL PHENOMENA

Weird episodes in the natural world

For centuries, with a total lack of rational explanations available, weird natural phenomena were attributed to the supernatural and witchcraft. Nowadays science can provide a logical account for much of the planet's natural phenomena, but even so, some of the world's goings on can still be fairly strange; it's not every day you expect to have frogs rain down on you from the skies; or look out your window to discover a fresh fall of orange snow.

Strange rains

Water isn't the only thing that falls from the sky. Rains of animals and other things are a recognised meteorological phenomenon. They are usually explained as being the result of a waterspout or tornado sucking things out of the sea, lakes, or garden ponds and up into the air, where they are held aloft by rising air for a while, only to rain down later. This explanation has several problems, however: There is no evidence that it is even possible; it has never been observed; and, crucially, it cannot explain many strange rains. Not all strange rains are of fish or other aquatic life, for instance, while those that are often involve only one type of animal, raising the question, how can a waterspout be so selective?

FACT

Between July 25 and September 23, 2001, the southern Indian state of Kerala was hit by showers of red rain so deeply coloured that the water looked like blood. Some scientists said the red colour was caused by extraterrestrial cells from a passing comet, but the real culprit was probably spores from algae or fungus.

Incidents of strange rains

When	Where	What rained down
Easter 1666	Stansted, England	Baby whiting, sprats and smelts
March 1830	Islay, Scotland	Fresh herrings
July 1841	Derby, England	Fish and frogs poured down during a thunderstorm
May 1867	Dublin, Ireland	Hazelnuts that had been preserved in a bog
1871	Bath, England	Marine shrimps encapsulated in jelly
1877	Memphis, Tennessee	Live snakes
August 1879	Lomond Hills, Scotland	Seaweed
October 1881	Milwaukee, Wisconsin	Spiders' webs, some over 18 m (60 ft) in length . . . but no spiders!
August 1890	Baghdad, Iraq	An edible substance (thought to be either desert lichen or tamarisk) fell during a heavy shower. The locals gathered it up and made it into bread – manna from heaven!
1897	Macerata, Italy	Millions of seeds from the Judas Tree dropped from a blood-coloured cloud
June 1901	Tillers Ferry, South Carolina	Catfish, perch and trout fell onto a field
June 1939	Trowbridge, England	Frogs
October 1947	Marksville, Louisiana	A variety of fish, including largemouth bass, goggle-eyes, minnows and hickory shad, some up to 25 cm (10 in) long
August 2000	Great Yarmouth, England	5 cm (2 in) long sprats

Coloured snow

Another surprisingly common weather phenomenon is coloured snow. Snow can come in many different colours, including red, orange, green, brown, blue and yellow. Sometimes it may be caused by dust in the atmosphere, but often it is caused by algae growing in snow that has already fallen.

Mighty winds

Hurricanes, tornadoes, cyclones and typhoons might seem at first glance to be names for the same thing and in one sense that is true – they are all types of storm that cause high winds and can be deadly. However, these weather anomalies (what else can enable a cow to fly or destroy a house in seconds?) have subtle differences that define them.

◆ **Tornadoes:** *A tornado is far smaller than a hurricane, cyclone or typhoon. It is a whirlwind: a column of air that rotates at enormous speeds and reaches down from the base of a storm cloud to the ground, where it sucks up dust and debris and causes lots of damage. Even the biggest tornado is 3 km (2 miles) across at most; usually they are about 75 m (240 ft) across.*

◆ **Cyclones, hurricanes and typhoons:** *Hurricanes and typhoons are different names for the same thing – massive tropical storms technically known as tropical cyclones. When these storms occur in the Atlantic/Caribbean regions they are known as hurricanes. When they occur in the Pacific regions they are called typhoons.*

BACKGROUND Project Vortex, the Dimmit tornado, south of Dimmitt, Texas on June 2, 1995.

Most destructive tornado

Tornadoes can travel across the ground fast: On March 18, 1925, the 'Tri-State Tornado' was clocked at 117 km/h (73 mph) as it travelled 352 km (219 miles) through Missouri, Illinois and Indiana, destroying an amazing 15,000 homes and killing 695 people. It was the most destructive tornado in American history, and possibly anywhere.

World's highest wind speed

The highest wind speed ever recorded on Earth was 512 km/h (318 mph), inside a tornado near Moore in Oklahoma on May 3, 1999. The tornado killed four people and destroyed 250 homes.

The biggest storm ever

The biggest and strongest storm ever recorded was 'Typhoon Tip', which formed over the Pacific in October 1979, and has been called a super-typhoon. At its largest, Tip was 2,173 km (1,350 miles) across – that's about half the size of the United States. On October 12 the pressure at the center of the storm was 870 millibars, which is the lowest pressure ever recorded at Earth's surface. Windspeed was as high as 258 km/h (160 mph).

Most destructive storm

The most destructive storm in history, in terms of the cost of the damage inflicted, was Hurricane Katrina, which hit the United States in late August 2005. Estimates of the damage caused vary between US$125 billion and $75 billion, but even the lowest figure easily dwarfs the next most expensive storm that hit the United States, 1992's Hurricane Andrew, which caused $21 billion of damage (in 2005 dollar value).

✳ FACT

Waialeale, in Hawaii, has an average of 335 rainy days a year, with nearly 2.5 cm (1 in) of rain falling every day. At the other end of the scale, Arica, in Chile, has an average of one rainy day every six years.

Winds of fire

In the Bible pillars of fire occasionally destroyed enemies of God. They might be based on a scientifically observed phenomenon – winds of such extreme heat that they scorch everything in their path.

For instance, in the summer of 1869 a fiery whirlwind crossed Cheatham County, Tennessee, and burned everything in its path. Horses were singed, woodland set on fire, haystacks set ablaze, and entire farmhouses were wrapped in flames. When the pillar of fire reached the river, it raised a column of steam and finally died out.

Meanwhile in 1860, an extremely hot wind about 91 m (100 yards) wide and with a temperature of 49°C (120°F) passed over the state of Georgia, scorching cotton crops and killing people.

ABOVE Lightning storm near Sterling, Colorado.

The light fantastic

Lightning is a spectacular lighting display (and a danger that one is warned against as a child: don't stand under a tree in a thunderstorm; get off the phone, you could be electrocuted.

Scientifically, it is an electrical discharge between a cloud and the ground. It works like this: Storm clouds build up enormous electrical charges, like balloons rubbed against a sweater but on a titanic scale. When some of this charge is discharged to the ground, the electrical current instantly turns the air through which it passes into a super-heated plasma similar to what you might find in the Sun. As this plasma is created it glows with tremendous brilliance and expands explosively, creating acoustic shockwaves we hear as thunder.

Lighting sometimes strikes twice

What we think of as a single flash of lightning is actually caused by multiple strokes – as many as 42 – following the same path between cloud and ground at intervals of around 30 milliseconds (i.e. 0.03 seconds). In total, a flash lasts around 0.25 seconds, but most of this is the period between strokes.

Weird lightning

Lightning remains something of a mystery to science. For instance, scientists still don't known exactly where lightning bolts get their energy. Equally mysterious are the many different forms it can take and the strange things it can do:

◆ **Ball lightning:** *In 1963, an aircraft passed through an electrical storm on a night flight from New York to Washington DC. The passengers saw a glowing sphere emerge from the cockpit area, pass down the aisle, and then suddenly disappear with a bang. It was probably ball lightning, which scientists refused to believe existed until this incident.*

◆ **Coloured lightning:** *One evening in May 1925, during a church service at North Cadbury, in Somerset, England, the congregation saw flashes of red lightning. In Ontario in 1927 people saw green lightning.*

◆ **Clear-sky lightning:** *In 1886, the captain of a ship heading for the United States from Britain saw a brilliant flash of lightning and heard a clap of thunder even though the sky was clear and the sun shining.*

◆ **Lightning that digs:** *During a thunderstorm in Kensington, New Hampshire, a lightning strike hit a field and made a hole about 30 cm (1 ft) in diameter and 9 m (30 ft) deep. It filled with water, becoming a useful well for the farm.*

◆ **Red sprites:** *Red sprites are flashes of reddish-coloured lightning that jump from the tops of the clouds into the stratosphere. They last for a few thousandths of a second but can be many miles wide.*

◆ **Blue jets:** *These are cone-shaped flashes of lightning that erupt from the center of a thunderstorm.*

Wild weather – meteorological extremes

As global warming kicks in we can expect the climate to become ever more unstable with greater extremes. Many of the records listed below may not stand for very long.

Most extreme temperatures ever recorded

- **Coldest:** *Vostok, Antartica: –89°C (–128°F)*

- **Hottest:** *Al Aziziyah, Libya; in 1922 it was 58°C (136°F) in the shade*

- **Fastest drop:** *Brownrig, Montana; the temperature dropped from 7 to –49°C (45 to –56°F) in one day*

- **Fastest rise:** *Spearfish, South Dakota; the temperature rose from –20 to 7°C (–4 to 45°F) in two minutes*

Most extreme places on Earth

- **Hottest place:** *Dalol, Denakil Depression, Ethiopia; annual average temperature is 34°C (93.2°F)*

- **Coldest place:** *Plateau Station, Antarctica; annual average temperature is –134°C (–56.7°F)*

- **Wettest place:** *Mawsynram, Assam, India; annual average rainfall is 1,187 cm (467 in). But the wettest year on record was August 1860 to July 1861, when 2,646 cm (1,042 in) of rain fell on Cherranpunji, India*

- **Driest place:** *Atacama Desert, Chile; average annual rainfall is 0.7 mm (0.03 in), but in many years there is no recordable precipitation at all*

FACT

The speed of a lightning bolt is not known. Some scientists think it may travel as fast as half the speed of light – an astonishing 145,000 km/sec (90,000 miles/sec). Others think it's more likely it travels at one-tenth the speed of light – a mere 30,000 km/sec (18,640 miles/sec).

Biggest hailstone

Surprisingly, the official sizes used by meteorologists to describe hailstones include 'baseball' and 'grapefruit'. The biggest ever hailstone is claimed to be a stone over 1 kg (2 lb), falling on the Gopalganj district of Bangladesh, on April 14, 1986.

ABOVE The largest recognised hailstone, Aurora, Nebraska.

The biggest officially recognized hailstone was one 17.8 cm (7 in) across that fell on Aurora, Nebraska, on June 22, 2003. It would have been traveling at over 160 km/h (100 mph). Something else to worry about when out in a storm without an umbrella. While rarely a threat to physical safety of humans, large hail results in nearly US$1 billion a year in damage to property such as crops, roofs and automobiles.

Cut in half, a hailstone has concentric rings like an onion, which reveals the number of times it travelled to the top of the storm before falling to Earth.

Killer waves

Tsunamis are waves caused by earthquakes and/or landslides, sometimes wrongly referred to as tidal waves. They are a well-known phenomenon, but in recent years scientists have also come to accept the existence of something they long denied – rogue or freak waves. These are giant waves that spontaneously develop out in the ocean and can destroy even the largest ships.

The highest ever recorded tsunami was 64 m (210 ft) high. It hit the Kamchatka Peninsula, on the eastern coast of Siberia, in 1737.

Tsunami warning signs

If there is not enough time for authorities to issue a tsunami warning it might help to know some of the warning signs.

◆ **Earthquake:** *a natural tsunami warning. If you feel the earth shake, head for higher ground immediately – you may only have a few minutes. Remember that an earthquake can trigger killer waves thousands of kilometres across the ocean many hours after the event generated a tsunami.*

◆ **Change in sea level:** *experts believe that a receding ocean may give people as much as five minutes' warning to evacuate the area. Many people make the mistake of going down to the beach to view the retreating ocean exposing the seafloor.*

◆ **Strange sounds:** *if you hear a strange noise, for example a roaring sound, don't go and investigate. Head for higher ground.*

◆ **Local wildlife:** *animals often have more acute senses than humans, and many sense a tsunami before humans can. So if you notice a lot of strange animal behaviour, and a general stampede for higher ground, it might be best to follow suit.*

Wind waves come and go without flooding higher areas.

Water flows in a circle.

Tsunamis run quickly over the land as a wall of water.

Water flows straight

Rogue waves

It is now accepted that rogue or freak waves more than 30 m (100 ft) high – the height of a 12-story building – occur several times a year around the world. Encounters with such a wave are often fatal.

When	Height	What happened
1881	Unrecorded	A solitary wave swept overboard all hands on deck of the barge Rosina. Later the same year all the crew were on deck when she was hit by another monster wave and once again everyone was washed overboard. The only survivor was a crewman sick in his bunk, who was rescued by a passing steamer.
December 1922	24 cm (80 ft)	The RMS Majestic encountered freakishly high waves in an Atlantic storm.
February 1925	23 m (75 ft)	The RMS Olympic was bound from Southampton to New York when she was hit by a gigantic wave that damaged her navigation bridge.
1966	7–9 m (25–30 ft)	The Italian liner Michelangelo was heading for New York when she encountered heavy seas southeast of Newfoundland. She was pounded continuously by massive waves, but suddenly a monster wave smashed into the ship. Parts of the superstructure gave way, windows 9 m (30 ft) above the waterline were crushed, and steel plates on the bow were torn away. Three people were killed and 12 injured.
January 1, 1995	18.6 m (61 ft)	Wave sensors on the Draupner oil platform in the North Sea obtained the first official measurement of a rogue or freak wave. The wave damaged the platform and proved that such waves did exist.
2004	15–40 m (50–130 ft)	During Hurricane Ivan, sensors on the seabed in the Gulf of Mexico measured many waves that were 15 m (50 ft) high, and one rogue wave that was 28 m (91 ft) high. Scientists estimated that at the center of the storm waves reached 40 m (130 ft).

Mountain high, valley deep

The Earth's surface has some pretty big wrinkles. The highest point on Earth is Mount Everest in Nepal, at 8,850 m (29,035 ft). The peak was reached for the first time on May 29, 1953. (Everest 'grew' by 2 m (7 ft) in 1999 after GPS technology gave a more accurate measurement than previously possible.)

However, if measured from the lowest point of its base in the Hawaiian Trough on the floor of the Pacific Ocean, the dormant Hawaiian volcano Mauna Kea, 4,206 m (13,799 ft) above sea level, is the tallest mountain in the world, with a total height of 10,206 m (33,780 ft).

Lowest point

The lowest point on the Earth's land surface is usually said to be the Dead Sea, on the Israel – Jordan border, which is 409 m (1,342 ft) below sea level. However, the actual land surface of Antarctica, depressed beneath its ice cap, is 2,538 m (8,327 ft) below sea level.

ABOVE Floating in the Dead Sea.

Eruptions and quakes

Recent years have seen some destructive earthquakes, but the resulting death tolls cannot compare with history's worst disasters.

Most destructive earthquake: *The most destructive earthquake ever recorded in terms of deaths caused was one that hit Shansi, in China, on January 23, 1556. It was probably a magnitude 8 quake and it killed approximately 830,000 people.*

Most destructive volcano: *In historical times the largest eruption was Mt. Tambora in Indonesia, in 1815, one of the four biggest eruptions in the last 10,000 years, and easily the biggest in recorded history. About 40 cubic km (10 cubic miles) of ash was blasted into the atmosphere, and 10,000 people were directly killed by the eruption. Crop loss and famine killed 80,000 more.*

Animals and earthquakes

A number of recorded historical incidents suggest that animals somehow 'know' when an earthquake is about to strike.

When	Where	What happened
373 BCE	Helike, Greece	Roman historian and naturalist Aelian records great masses of mice, weasels, snakes and other small creatures marching along the road five days before the earthquake that destroyed the city.
1783	Messina, Sicily	Dogs were howling so much before the great earthquake that men went with cudgels to kill them. After the event, local folk left their houses at the slightest howling of dogs.
1835	Talcahuano, Chile	All the dogs left the city and headed for the open countryside prior to the earthquake. The previous day, huge flocks of seabirds were seen to fly inland at Concepcion.

Earth's strangest places

Some of the weirdest places on Earth are also among the least known.

A giant heap of bat poo

Deer Cave in Malaysia is a massive cavern into which London's St. Paul's Cathedral could fit five times over, but it's what is inside the cave that makes it so incredible. The cave is home to millions of bats, with at least twelve species, probably the greatest variety known for a single cave, which fly out each night to massacre the insect life of the surrounding rainforest. At the peak exit time 200,000 bats a minute stream out into the dusk. Since each bat eats about 10 g (1/3 oz) of insects, some 16 tons of bugs are gobbled each night, and a lot of this then comes out of the other end of the roosting bats – about 5 tons of fresh guano (bat dung) per night. This falls to the floor of the cave, where it has built up into the largest pile of bat crap on the planet.

Insects like to eat nitrogen-rich bat dung, which makes the Deer Cave dung heap a juicy prospect for tens of millions of cockroaches, flies, maggots, beetles, bugs, millipedes, springtails, worms and other invertebrates, and for the millions of spiders and scorpions, snakes and other creatures that eat them. The Deer Cave heap has the highest concentration of cockroaches on the planet, and they are so dense that the surface of the heap looks like running water.

FACT
Every day at least one volcano is erupting somewhere in the world.

The crystal caves

Lechuguilla Cave in Carlsbad Caverns National Park in the United States is one of the most incredible, but also least visited, places on Earth. It is 193 km (120 miles) long and up to 500 m (1,650 ft) underground. Carved out of the limestone by sulfuric acid, which was created by sulfurous gases bubbling up from volcanic vents and dissolving in groundwater, the caves are remarkable because of their huge and delicate gypsum crystal formations. Normally caves are too wet for crystals to survive, as the crystal formations dissolve in water, but Lechuguilla is warm and dry. Some of the crystals are as big as chandeliers. Only a tiny handful of people have been allowed in as the unique crystal formations could so easily be damaged by human exposure; the ecosystem in the caves is so fragile that every single item of food, equipment and waste that is brought in must also be taken out.

BELOW Stalagmites, stalactites and draperies by a pool in Lechuguilla Cave.

The lake that has never seen the Sun

Buried underneath 4 km (2.5 miles) of Antarctic ice is Lake Vostok, the largest sub-glacial lake in the world. It is about 250 km (155 miles) long by 50 km (31 miles) wide at its widest point, and 800 m (2,625 ft) deep at its deepest point. Although the average water temperature is 26.6°F (−3°C), the freshwater in the lake remains unfrozen because of the huge pressure of ice bearing down on it. The lake was formed between 500,000 and 1 million years ago, and is thought to be the closest terrestrial equivalent to conditions on the Jupiter moon of Europa, a possible incubator of extraterrestrial life (see page 47). Incredibly, there is bacterial life in Lake Vostok, even though the water there has never seen the Sun and has oxygen concentrations 50 times higher than normal freshwater, which makes it highly toxic.

The lake that disappeared

Until the 1960s the Aral Sea was the world's fourth largest lake. By 2004 it had shrunk to a quarter of its original size, going from 68,000 square km (26,255 square miles) to 17,160 square km (6,625 square miles), and less than a fifth of its volume. This appalling ecological tragedy was caused by the redirection of most of the water that flows into the lake to poorly managed cotton irrigation projects. Cotton is one of the thirstiest crops, while the irrigation canals lost up to 80 percent of the water to evaporation.

Now the Aral Sea has shrunk so much it has split into two parts. The northern remnant may be saved, but the southern one is expected to vanish within 15 years. The real problem is that the evaporated lake has left huge salt flats that are loaded with highly toxic heavy metals and other pollution, which is now picked up by huge dust storms and is poisoning crops and people around the lake. The climate of the region has also become more extreme.

Singing sands, ringing rocks and waterguns

Some regions of the world are renowned for the mysterious sounds you can hear. These are tied to their geographic locale, but can be difficult or impossible to explain.

◆ **Waterguns:** *This is one of many terms for rumbling noises like thunder or cannons heard near bodies of water. Other names include* **mistpoeffers** *in the Netherlands,* **brontidi** *in Italy,* **retumbos** *in the Philippines, 'lake guns' or, best of all, 'sea farts'. Places to hear them include beaches in Wilmington County, North Carolina; Old Hannah's Caves, Staffordshire, England; and the North Sea between Britain and Northern Europe. One theory is that they are caused when pockets of methane in the sea or lakebed erupt like a giant belch.*

◆ **The Moodus noises:** *The local Native Americans regarded the area now known as East Haddam, Connecticut, as a sacred place because of the prevalence of thundering noises and earth tremors. They called it* **Morehemoodus***, or 'the noisy place'. The US Geological Survey dismisses them as minor tremors but this is not supposed to be an area of seismic activity.*

◆ **Singing sand dunes:** *There are 35 known places around the world where sand dunes can be heard to make a booming or rumbling noise, giving them the name 'singing sand'. Marco Polo heard them in the Gobi Desert in the 13th century, and today the best place to hear them is the Atlantic Sahara in Morocco. The noises are caused by small avalanches of sand sliding down the faces of dunes. The colliding sand grains generate a small wave of noise, which feeds back on itself so that the movement of the grains is coordinated and the surface of the dune acts like a loudspeaker – a loud, steady noise results.*

◆ **Ringing rocks:** *These are rocks and boulders that look normal but ring like a bell when struck with a hammer or other tool. A well-known location is Ringing Rocks Park in Bucks County, Pennsylvania. In June 1890 a local doctor collected a range of ringing rocks from here and, accompanied by a brass band, used them to put on a concert for the Buckwampum Historical Society.*

BIZARRE
ANIMALS AND
WEIRD PLANTS

Weird wildlife

There have been stories of strange, and often mythical, animals and plants for centuries. But there are enough strange plants and critters living on our planet already without needing to resorting to fiction and fairytales. Some have developed unique ways of hunting or avoid being hunted. Others possess suprising levels of intelligence and some creatures gain our attention by being just plain odd-looking, but they are all unique and fascintating in their own weird ways.

Animal magic

Through the evolutionary process animals adapt to their environments, and this can lead to some extraordinary shapes, behaviours, and abilities. Here are just a few of the weird and wonderful examples from the animal kingdom.

Slime

Slime is produced when animals excrete long protein molecules that mix with water to produce a sticky, oozing substance. Slime helps to protect and shield animals, and also as lubrication to help them move.

FACT

The fulmar is a seabird that looks like a gull. It has a revolting secret weapon it uses to defend itself while nesting. If threatened it can vomit a foul-smelling noxious substance called 'stomach oil', which is made up of partially digested shrimp, squid and fish, and shoot it up to 2 m (6.5 ft). Stomach oil matts the feathers of enemy birds, ruining their waterproofing and flying abilities. Even the name 'fulmar' means 'foul bird'.

◆ **Slug slime:** Slugs need slime to stop them drying out and to help them slide around. Slug slime can absorb enormous amounts of water – you could soak up an entire bathtub full of water with just 1 L (2 pints) of slug slime. It's such amazing stuff that scientists are studying it to see if it can be used for tasks from cleaning up sewage to protecting wounds in hospitals.

◆ **Banana slug slime:** The banana slug has slime that tastes of bananas (although it's not clear who was weird enough to discover this in the first place).

ABOVE A banana slug's slime has a number of purposes: protection against predators; movement; respiration; and attracting mates

◆ **Hagfish slime:** The hagfish is perhaps the most revolting fish in the sea. They are ugly and pale and eat just about anything. To protect themselves they produce slime from hundreds of pores all over their body. So much comes out that an enemy fish can be suffocated in great gobs of the stuff. If you put a hagfish in a bucket of water, the bucket will soon overflow with horrible slime produced by the agitated fish.

◆ **Parrotfish slime:** Each night on tropical coral reefs, parrotfish surround themselves with a cocoon of slime, like a sleeping bag. It stops their smell from seeping into the water and alerting nocturnal predators, such as sharks and moray eels.

Dung insulation

A home lined with bug-attracting dung, anyone? This is exactly how the burrowing owl likes it. The burrowing owl makes its nest in tunnels or burrows in the ground, and when nesting during the breeding season, it lines the inside of the burrow with cow dung, which attracts bugs, which the owl then eats. The dung also acts like loft insulation, helping to keep the temperature steady.

Sticky-footed lizard

Geckos are lizards known for their ability to run along walls and ceilings. On each foot is a special pad that is covered in about 500,000 tiny bristles, each of which in turn sprouts thousands of tiny fibers that look like mini cauliflowers in close-up. This means that each foot has millions of points where it makes contact with the surface on which the lizard is standing, and each of these points uses something similar to a static electric charge to stick to that surface. The combined stickiness is so powerful that an average-sized 12-year-old could hang from a gecko and it would still stick to the ceiling.

LEFT Fake tongue louse.

Fake tongue louse

Isopods are a group of crustaceans that includes woodlice, although most types live in the sea. One type of isopod, *Cymothoa exigua*, is a parasite that lives in the rose snapper fish. It gets into its host's mouth, eats away the tongue and then sits in its place, pretending to be the fish's own tongue and feeding on particles of food the fish catches.

Here's blood in your eye!

The Texas horned lizard is an ugly critter covered in warts, spines and spikes. But its real secret weapon is the ability to squirt blood out of the corner of its eyes. Sinuses (air spaces) behind the eye fill up with blood and are then squeezed until the blood spurts out – up to 1 m (3 ft). The blood is mixed with a horrible chemical that makes it taste foul to coyotes, cats, dogs and other predators that the lizard fears.

Skunk stench

Skunks are renowned for their horrible smell that they can spray from their behinds. In fact it's how they got their name, which is a version of the Algonquin Indian word *segonku* – 'one who squirts'. The Latin name of the most common species of skunk is *Mephitis mephitis*, which translates as 'stench stench', while the name of another species, *Spilogale putorius*, means 'stinking spotted weasel'.

The stench is made up of sulfurous chemicals secreted by glands inside the anus. Strong muscles allow it to be squirted in a precise direction for up to 3 m (10 ft). The stench is so powerful it can be smelled up to a mile away, and can cause blindness and vomiting.

Foul play

The phrase 'playing possum' is another way of saying 'playing dead' and comes from the cunning trick used by the opossum, a cat-sized creature that looks like a cross between a badger and a weasel. If threatened it takes advantage of the fact that most animals steer clear of dead or diseased prey in case of contamination, and so pretends to be dead. It lies on its side, foaming at the mouth with its lips drawn back and its tongue lolling out, poos itself and, most unpleasantly of all, fouls itself with fluid from its anus that smells like rotting flesh.

Master of disguise

The mimic octopus has amazingly fine control of its skin colour and the shapes it can make using its body and tentacles, which it uses to imitate scary or poisonous creatures in order to frighten predators. It can make itself look exactly like a poisonous lionfish or a tangle of venomous sea snakes. In fact, it is so good at mimicking other animals that it was not discovered until 1998. Before this, divers who had seen it simply thought they were seeing one of the animals it mimics.

Missile-firing tarantulas

Tarantulas are big, hairy spiders and are found all over the world. Many species grow special hair on their abdomens and back legs, which form part of their defence against predators. The hairs are irritating and can even be lethal to humans. Some species are able to fire these hairs like darts by 'kicking them off' – they turn around and aim their butts at attackers, and then rub their hind legs against the butt, knocking off the hairs and throwing them at the enemy. This can leave the predator with irritating and allergy-causing hairs in their mouths, noses and even eyes.

Oldest organisms

Some types of plant, fungus and bacteria reproduce by cloning. Some spores of fungi and bacteria found in ancient tombs are thousands of years old but can come to life in the right conditions. Theoretically these are the oldest organisms on Earth. Discounting these, the oldest living things are:

◆ **Plants:** *Bristlecone pine called Methuselah that is 4,767 years old. It grows in the White Mountains, California.*

◆ **Animals:** *Madagascar radiated tortoise called Tui Malila which reached the age of at least 188 before it died in 1965.*

◆ **Other contenders:** *There are other animals whose age has been determined indirectly. Growth rings in the Ocean Quahog, a type of clam, show that at least one specimen lived for 220 years. Also cold-seep, deep-sea tubeworms grow incredibly slowly but are thought to live for 250 years or more based on their size.*

Man-eaters and cold-blooded killers

What's the world's most dangerous animal? It depends on what you mean by dangerous – the one that's killed the most people, the most poisonous, or the one you'd least like to meet in a dark alley?

RIGHT Mexican redknee tarantula. Defences include kicking irritating hairs at attackers, running away or, as a last resort, biting the predator.

Mass murderers

♦ **Plasmodium:** *The parasite that causes malaria. This microscopic evildoer has probably killed more people than any other animal in history – it is thought to have been responsible for half of all natural deaths since the Stone Age.*

♦ **Houseflies and mosquitoes:** *These are probably the next biggest killers after creatures that cause diseases directly. They spread diseases like dysentery and malaria.*

♦ **Humans:** *Mankind itself is pretty dangerous and has killed hundreds of millions of people throughout history.*

The most poisonous

The usual criteria are: How many people can one animal's venom kill, and how fast does the venom work?

♦ **Most venomous creature in the world:** *The Australian box jellyfish, or sea wasp. Each jellyfish contains enough poison to kill 60 humans in as little as four minutes.*

♦ **Most dangerous venomous creatures in the world:** *Probably bees and wasps, because their toxin causes severe allergic reactions that kill hundreds or even thousands of people around the world each year.*

♦ **Most venomous snake in the world:** *The inland taipan or fierce snake, from central Australia. Each bite contains enough venom to kill up to 100 humans.*

♦ **Most dangerous venomous snake:** *The carpet viper, found from West Africa to India, which is less toxic than the taipan but kills more people than any other species. Its venom causes massive bleeding.*

♦ **Most venomous spider:** *The six-eyed sand spider, found in southern Africa. Although shy and reclusive, it has very powerful venom that rots flesh and causes massive bleeding, and to which there is no antidote.*

♦ **Most venomous fish:** *The stonefish, found in the Indian and Pacific Oceans. If stepped on, the spines on its back act like hypodermic needles, injecting poison that causes death within six hours.*

Animals you'd least like to meet in a dark alley

This depends on a combination of size, weapons (i.e. teeth, claws, and so on) and, above all, aggression. Some really scary animals actually aren't that aggressive and generally avoid humans given a chance. Sharks are a good example – they rarely target humans and usually only because they've mistaken them for seals. Here are the top five animals you should really try to avoid:

1. **Hippo:** *Hippos can weigh up to 3.5 tons and run at up to 30 km/h (18 mph). They have enormous teeth and can easily bite a man in half. Worst of all, they are mean – they will aggressively target humans, and particularly like to upset boats and then chomp the passengers. Hippos are said to be the most dangerous large animal in Africa in terms of your chances of actually being killed by one.*

2. **African or Cape buffalo:** *An alternative claimant to the title of big animal that kills most people in Africa is the buffalo. They are highly aggressive, powerful, and very fast, able to reach top speeds of 56 km/h (35 mph) and outrun lions if given a head start. Old males can weigh up to 2000 lbs (900 kg) or more. Big game hunters prized them above almost all other game, and told tales of cunning buffalo who would stalk hunters, chase them up trees, flick stinging urine at them with their tales and savage their corpses for hours.*

RIGHT Saltwater Crocodile, the largest of all living reptiles.

3. **Saltwater crocodile:** *Although encounters between humans and saltwater, or estuarine, crocs are rare – so that few people are actually killed by them each year – these are very scary creatures. They can be immense – up to 7 m (23 ft) long and weighing over 1 ton. And they can both swim fast and sprint faster than a horse over a short distance. They are highly aggressive and eat anything, including sharks and water buffalo. Their tails can break legs and spines, and their jaws can crush a skull like an egg. They will sneak up on prey and launch themselves out of the water like a missile.*

4. **Grizzly bear:** *Grizzlies have claws up to 15 cm (6 in) long, weigh up to 680 kg (1,500 lb), and can run at up to 55 km/h (34 mph). Even the somewhat larger polar bear is afraid of the grizzly for their stronger muscles, denser bones, and pure strength. But most frightening of all, they combine aggression with curiosity - a lethal combination for humans*

5. **Siberian tiger:** *The largest of the cat family, tigers are equipped with a fearsome array of weaponry. They have bigger and longer canines than even lions, their size and power means they can knock over animals much bigger than themselves, and they have huge, muscular forelimbs – a single blow from one paw can instantly kill an adult wolf or large deer. Tigers can swim, run fast and leap up to 10 m (33 ft) in the air. They can even leap over obstacles more than 2 m (6 ft) high while carrying a whole deer. Siberian tigers are the biggest of all, with adult males weighing up to 800 lb (350 kg). They have been known to kill and eat adult bears. On the whole, however, tigers are shy and not aggressive and only become man-eaters when they are desperate or too old and sick to catch normal prey.*

✳ FACT

Elephants are also among the world's most potentially dangerous animals, capable of crushing and killing any other land animal, from rhinocerous and lions to humans. It is thought they may kill up to 500 people every year.

Shark attack facts and figures

According to the International Shark Attack File there were 62 shark attacks in the world in 2006, only four of which were fatal. Data from previous years shows this is pretty average.

The worst place for shark attacks is Florida, which is probably because there are more people in the water there than anywhere else.

Shark and dog attack fatalities in the United States

To put shark attack figures in perspective, compare them to the figures for dog attacks.

Year	Number of fatal shark attacks	Number of fatal dog attacks
2002	0	15
2003	1	26
2004	2	22
2005	1	28
2006	4	31

What to do in a shark attack

If you are unlucky enough to get cornered by a shark, it might be useful to have an escape plan.

◆ *Try to keep still. Sharks are attracted by movement and splashing. Remain still and with any luck it will lose interest.*

◆ *If it comes too close for comfort, aim a blow to a vulnerable area. The snout, eyes and gills are good target areas for deterring an attack.*

◆ *Remember: sharks are attracted to blood. Their keen noses can detect one drop of blood in 100 litres of water (25 gallons) and can smell blood 0.4 km (0.25 miles) away.*

Animal death matches

The most important question in biology is, of course, which animal is the hardest? Normally big predators don't meet in the wild because they have evolved to live in different areas, but humans have sometimes pitted them against one another.

Lion vs tiger

The biggest tigers are bigger and stronger than lions, but they are less used to fighting other big cats – tigers live mostly solitary lives, while lions are social creatures. Also, the tiger's typical attack method is to land a lethal bite to the back of the neck, but lions have a shaggy mane that protects them. Evidence from the circus – in Roman times, when it involved death matches, and in modern times, when animals are put together for shows and sometimes fight – proves that lions almost always win, unless the tiger can figure out how to get around that mane.

Lion vs grizzly bear

Californian gold miners in the 19th century pitted grizzly bears against both bulls and lions. The grizzlies won easily, smashing in the other creatures' heads with single blows from their paws. Grizzlies have dense bones and heavy, powerful muscles, while big cats have light bones and elastic muscles to give them agility and speed.

King Kong vs T. Rex

It's the ultimate animal celebrity death match – monster gorilla King Kong or fearsome king of the dinosaurs *Tyrannosaurus rex*? King Kong is about 7.6 m (25 ft) high, with an advanced primate's brain, super-strong arms and legs, amazing agility and balance, and prehensile hands that can pick up tools. *T. Rex* was typically about 5 m (16 ft) tall

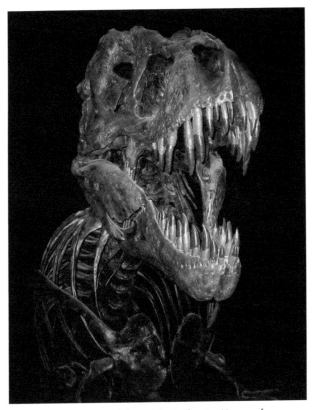

ABOVE Tyrannosaurus rex skeleton at the Smithsonian Museum of Natural History.

and 43 ft (13 m) long, with massive daggerlike teeth and the strongest bite of any dinosaur.

According to a panel of experts consulted by *Forbes* magazine, Kong would win a match-up between the two monsters, by virtue of his superior intelligence, strength and ability. The fight would not last long as Kong would simply jump on the dinosaur's back and break its neck.

Amazing insects and astonishing arthropods

Insects are part of a larger group of animals called arthropods, which also includes crabs, spiders, shrimps and many others. Arthropods are by far the most diverse and most numerous group of animals. What follows are some of the weirdest, wildest and grossest examples of the arthropod world.

Jumping jack flash

The English spittlebug *Philaenus spumarius* is the world's highest jumper. It can jump 75 cm (27.5 in) straight up, the equivalent of a person jumping over a 70-story building.

Armed and dangerous

Snapping shrimps, or pistol shrimps, have a specialised claw that can snap shut at such enormous speed and with such pressure that it creates a shock wave powerful enough to kill small fish and break glass up to 1.8 m (6 ft) away. The snapping creates tiny bubbles called 'cavitation bubbles', which implode with such force that they momentarily generate temperatures as hot as the surface of the Sun. The noise made by snapping shrimps is so loud a submarine can pass undetected through an area where they are active.

Super-shrimp – the world's most powerful animal?

The mantis shrimp also uses specialised claws that snap shut with amazing force, but it uses them to smash enemies and

FACT

The mantis shrimp is a delicacy in China, where it is used in a dish known as 'pissing shrimp' because the mantis shrimp urinates itself when put in a cooking pot. Well, wouldn't you?

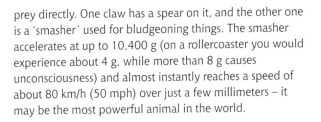

prey directly. One claw has a spear on it, and the other one is a 'smasher' used for bludgeoning things. The smasher accelerates at up to 10,400 g (on a rollercoaster you would experience about 4 g, while more than 8 g causes unconsciousness) and almost instantly reaches a speed of about 80 km/h (50 mph) over just a few millimeters – it may be the most powerful animal in the world.

Exploding beetles

The bombardier beetle has an explosive behind. In a chamber at the tip of its abdomen it mixes chemicals that set off an explosion. The resulting scalding hot liquid can be squirted at predators, and as the abdomen can be rotated through 270 degrees, it can hit an aggressor attacking from almost any direction.

Boxing glove crab

The boxer crab, or pom-pom crab, grows a pair of stinging sea anemones, one on each claw, which it waves around like boxing gloves or pom-poms, hence the name.

BELOW The boxer crab is found in the tropical Indo-west Pacific. The crabs carapace can reach 1.5 cm (half an inch) in length.

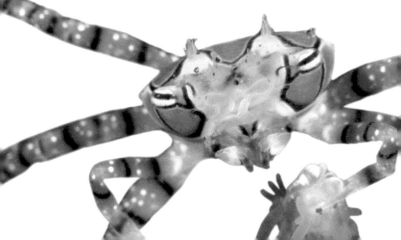

Poison plants

Many plant species have evolved poisons to put off animals that want to eat them. Possibly the most toxic plant is the castor oil plant – its beans contain the extremely toxic substance ricin, and just one or two of them can kill a person. There is also a whole family of plants called the *Solanaceae*, which contain substances called alkaloids and includes species such as deadly nightshade, jimsonweed, foxglove and datura. These can be used in medicine, but in high enough doses they are toxic; just three nightshade berries can kill a child.

Probably the most poisonous mushroom is the death cap, one of the *Amanita* species, most of which are toxic. Eating as little as 50 g (2 oz) of death cap can be fatal. Half of all deaths from eating mushrooms are caused by the death cap, with other members of the *Amanita* family causing 45 of the other 50 per cent.

ABOVE *Amanita phalloide*, commonly know as the death cap.

FACT
Potato beetle larvae have a horrible habit. To protect themselves against predators they cover themselves in their own toxic poo! Not surprisingly, this tends to deter some would-be predators.

Psychic pets and intelligent animals

Animals can be cleverer than you think; some of them may even have psychic powers. Many pet owners swear that their animals can tell what they are thinking. One piece of evidence often put forward is that you can tell when a dog's owner is about to come home because it will get very excited before it could possibly have heard or smelled its master.

Toby the thinking pig

Before television people had to get their entertainment elsewhere. Performing animals were popular, but none was as accomplished as Toby the Sapient Pig, a star attraction of the early 19th century. Toby could apparently read, spell, do maths, play cards, tell the time and, most astonishingly of all, read minds. He would communicate by stamping his feet or pointing to things with his snout. He became a sensation, packing out theatres, and was such a celebrity that in 1818 someone brought out his 'autobiography'.

Was Toby really intelligent and psychic? Possibly he was simply well trained and could pick up on minute signals from his owner that told him what to do, but which no one else could recognise.

Clever Hans the horse

In the late 19th and early 20th centuries, a horse known as Clever Hans was the toast of Germany for his apparent ability to tap out the answers to maths questions, and questions put into numerical form. A psychologist later claimed to have proved that Hans did not actually understand the questions or know the answers, but simply kept tapping until he could tell by looking at the person asking the question that he had reached the right number.

Top five most intelligent animals

This list of intelligent animals is not official, but represents the range of intelligence in the animal world:

1. **Chimps and other great apes:** *Chimps are the closest animals to humans, and seem to be roughly equivalent in intelligence to a small child. Both chimps and gorillas can be taught sign language and have been known to ask for pets, express emotion and even to proposition their human trainers.*

2. **Dolphins and other cetaceans:** *The bottlenose dolphin can learn simple sentences, so that it can be asked to do something that it has never done before and successfully complete the task. In the wild, dolphins are known to communicate with each other, form complex social communities and even to have what looks like culture.*

3. **Grey parrots:** *Research has shown that African grey parrots can apparently learn up to a thousand words, understand them, and even combine them into new sentences.*

4. **Octopi:** *Considered to be the most intelligent animal without a backbone, the octopus is at least as intelligent as the average house cat. Octopi can apparently communicate by changing colours, can remember and learn (including by watching other octopi), can figure out how to open jars and get through mazes, and can distinguish between different shapes, patterns and colours. One problem is that they are so intelligent they can figure out how to get out of an aquarium. They have even been known to break into the holds of fishing boats to gorge on crabs.*

5. **Mantis shrimp:** *Even something as small as a mantis shrimp (see page 86) seems to show a surprisingly high level of intelligence. Mantis shrimps can signal to each other using fluorescent lights on their bodies, and may even be able to 'talk' to other species. They can learn new behaviours and can remember other individual shrimps.*

BEING
HUMAN

There's a freak in all of us

We may think the world around us is weird, but as we stop and stare at the world's freaky anomalies, we should probably keep in mind that humans themselves can be pretty strange too. Even the everyday functions of the human body which we take for granted, like our senses, can be truly astounding if you stop to think about them. The human body is capable of producing a fascinating variety of gross bodily fluids; it gets assualted by numberless nasty diseases out to get us; and can suffer from some unusal mutations. And that's just the physical side, without even delving into the strange and disturbing world of the human conscious mind and all that it's capable of.

Bewildering body bits

The statistics about the human body are truly astounding. Read the selection of facts and figures below and you may never look at yourself in the mirror in the same way.

Estimates of the number of **cells in the human body** vary widely, partly because the numbers involved are so huge that it's impossible actually to count them. An average estimate is that there are about 75 trillion cells in the human body – that's 75,000,000,000,000.

Incredibly, there are **ten times as many bacteria** cells living in your gut as there are in the rest of your whole body – also about 750 trillion.

FACT
Up to 60 per cent of the solid part of your poo is not made up of food, but of bacteria from your gut.

Brain facts

There are about 100 billion nerve cells in the adult human brain, but ten times as many support cells to look after them.

The nerve cells form connections with each other, which allows them to 'talk' to one another. There are an estimated 100 trillion connections between the nerve cells, which is more than there are leaves in the Amazon rainforest.

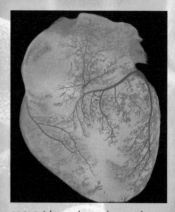

ABOVE A human heart, showing the arteries and veins which supply blood to the cardiac muscles.

Adults lose, on average, about 100,000 nerve cells from their brain every day. Over the course of a lifetime, this adds up to losing about 7 per cent of the brain.

Heart and blood

- The heart beats about 100,000 times a day without rest for an entire lifetime – that's more than 2.5 billion beats in a lifetime.

- Laid end to end, a child's blood vessels would stretch for over 96,600 kms (60,000 miles); an adult's for 161,000 km (100,000 miles) – that's four times around the Equator.

- The blood of an adult man contains more than 25 trillion cells.

- One drop of blood contains over 250 million cells.

- Nearly 3 million red blood cells die every second (but don't worry – they're replaced at the same rate).

- An average red blood cell lives for only 120 days. During this time it will travel 480 km (300 miles) on its journey round and round the body.

Bones, skin, hair and nails

Human bone is as strong as iron, but three times lighter. But if you soak a bone in hydrochloric acid over night, all the minerals will be removed, and you can tie it in a knot.

During the day gravity presses down on you and your spine compresses. When you lie down for a night's sleep, your **spine rebounds** to its normal length. This means that come the morning you may be up to 2.5 cm (1 in) taller than you were the previous evening.

One person in 20 has an **extra rib**, and it is three times as common in men as in women.

6.5 square cm (one square inch) of **human skin** has 19 million cells, 60 hairs, 90 oil glands, 5.8 m (19 ft) of blood vessels, and 625 sweat glands. If this patch of skin is on your forearm there will be around 10,000 bacteria on it; if it is in your armpit, there could be 1 million bacteria.

Fingernails grow twice to four times as fast as toenails. The nail on the middle finger grows fastest. If you lose a toenail it takes about six months to grow back completely.

Not the man you used to be

Most of the parts of your body are constantly recycled, with old cells dying and being replaced by new ones. Different parts are renewed at different rates – an adult's skin regenerates about once a month, while over a year between 10 and 30 per cent of an adult's skeleton is replaced. Over the course of three years almost every cell in your body has been replaced by new ones, making you literally a different person to who you were two years ago.

Sperm-tastic

The average adult male produces 50,000 sperm per minute – that's 72 million per day. A single male ejaculation contains 200 million sperm – theoretically enough to generate the combined population of Britain, France and Germany. Each sperm leaving the penis travels at 8,000 body lengths per second, equivalent to a human swimming at 54,700 km/h (34,000 mph).

Organs you can live without

It is possible for machines and medication to fill in for most missing or malfunctioning organs for at least some period of time. However, there are a number of organs that you could afford to lose without needing anything to replace them.

◆ **Appendix:** *Contrary to popular belief this organ is not completely useless, as it plays a role in the immune system, but many people have them removed to combat appendicitis, and they live happily ever after.*

◆ **Gall bladder:** *This is an ugly little baglike organ that makes bile, which helps digestion, but you can live without it and it is often removed as part of treatment for gallstones.*

◆ **Kidney:** *You can get by with just one, although you would need to be extra careful about what you eat and drink.*

◆ **Spleen:** *This organ helps look after blood cells and is an important part of the immune system. You can live without it, because other organs can fill in for it, although it would weaken your immune system.*

◆ **Liver:** *This is one of the most important organs in the body, but it has the amazing ability to regenerate itself, so you can lose up to 75 per cent and it will grow back. However, to survive long enough for this to happen you would need serious intensive care.*

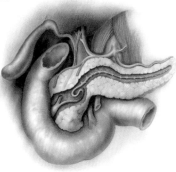

RIGHT A normal pancreas and gall bladder.

Stupendous senses

Humans have evolved a range of senses to help us navigate the natural world. It is widely thought that there are only five senses, however in addition to taste, smell, vision, hearing and touch, we have senses of balance and proprioception (a sense of where the parts of your body are in relation to one another).

Smell

You have about 5 million smell cells in your nose. They make your sense of smell 10,000 times more sensitive than your sense of taste. When your sense of smell is at its best (when you are young, as olfaction degrades with age), you can differentiate between 4–10,000 different smells.

Vision

Vision involves the cells of the retina, at the back of the eye. Light falls onto cells calls rods and cones. The cones are for perceiving colour, while the rods are for perceiving light and dark. You have about 120 million rods in each retina, but only about 7 million cones.

The rods are 100 times more sensitive to light than the cones and function even when it is dark. This is why in low light you perceive the world in shades of grey. In fact a rod cell can respond to as little as a single photon of light, which is the amount of light that would reach a human eye from a candle 1.6 km (a mile) away.

> **FACT**
> Diabetes can lead to high levels of sugar in the urine. Before simple tests for sugar levels were available, doctors would taste their patients' urine to see if was sweet!

Touch

Each square centimeter of your skin contains around 200 pain receptors, 15 pressure receptors, and seven temperature receptors – six for low and one for high temperatures.

Taste

The cells in the taste bud are renewed at the rate of roughly one every ten hours, while the taste bud as a whole has a typical lifespan of about ten days. There are about 10,000 taste buds in the mouth. Each contains about 50–100 receptor cells, which have tiny hairs that pick up taste molecules from food, drink and the air. Each of these cells is specialized to respond to one of the five primary tastes.

Five primary tastes

Taste	Foods & substances
Sour	Hydrogen ions; lime, lemon, tamarind
Sweet	Carbohydrates; sucrose (table sugar), fructose, some amino acids, like glycine
Bitter	Caffeine (coffee); quinine (tonic water); banana peel
Salty	Sodium ions; table salt and foods with a high salt content
Umami	From the Japanese for savoury or meaty. Protein-rich foods and artificial flavourings; meat, cheese, mushrooms

Hearing

Sound is produced by vibrations, and vibrations are measured in terms of frequency, the unit of which is Hertz (Hz). Humans can hear sounds in the range 20 Hz up to 20,000 Hz (by contrast with rats, for instance, which can hear from 1,000 to 50,000 Hz). The most sensitive range of human hearing is between 1000 and 4000 Hz.

Table of decibel levels and effects

The decibel is a logarithmic unit, which means that it is a ratio rather than a dimension. It also means that 2 decibels is not twice as loud as 1 but an order of magnitude (i.e.10 times) louder.

Decibel level	Equivalent sound/effect on human
-4 to +4	Ticking of an ordinary wristwatch at a distance of 1 m (3.3 feet)
0	Whine of a mosquito 3 m (10 feet) away
40	A human whisper
60	A norma conversation
100	Average house or car stereo at maximum volume
120–130	Front row at a rock concert
127	Tinnitus (ringing in the ears) caused
140	Even momentary exposure causes hearing damage
145	Vision blurs as eyeballs vibrate
147	Formula 1 car
150	Sound registered at concert by The Who
152	Vibrations in body painful; joint pain
153	Throat vibrations make swallowing impossible
154	Loud enough to pop a balloon
165	Jet engine at take-off
172	Sound waves cause water vapour to condense into fog
200	Fatal

Gross bodily fluids

The human body produces a wide range of secretions. Some, such as mucus, have protective/defensive functions. Fluids such as urine, are excretory in nature, and help to get rid of the by-products of metabolism. Fluids such as blood combine many functions, transporting nutrients and waste and carrying immune system cells and clotting factors for defense.

Urine

The average person produces about 1.4 L (3 pints) of urine a day. Urine is sterile, so the wee you produce is actually cleaner than your hands after they've just been washed. This is why it's not dangerous to drink, and it can even be useful as a topical ointment – for instance to treat jellyfish stings.

How long can you hold on? In a normal adult the bladder rarely holds more than about 320 ml (¾ pint) of urine, with the urge to urinate coming at the 280 ml (½ pint) mark. More than 500 ml (1 pint) causes pain and an intense urge to urinate immediately.

Spit

Most people produce 3.8 L (8 pints) of spit a day. It's produced by the three sets of salivary glands around the mouth area. That works out at about 24,000 L (50,700 pints) produced in the average lifetime – enough to fill a couple of large swimming pools.

FACT
In Roman times gladiators would brush their teeth with urine and then gargle with it too. They believed it was good for their gums. What's even more amazing is that the ladies used to go wild for gladiators, who were the pop idols of their day.

Vomit

Children have a much lower vomiting threshold than adults. One person vomiting often sets off other people. A possible reason for this is that early humans, like today's apes, used to travel around in groups, feeding off the same tree or food source, and it made sense if one member of the group was sick (because there was something wrong with the food) for everyone else to follow suit.

Compared to other animals, however, humans are relatively light on vomiting. Big vegetarian whales vomit every 7 to 10 days to help get rid of anything inedible they may have swallowed by accident. Dogs not only vomit frequently, they will eat their own vomit. Probably the most vomitous animals, however, are cows, who digest otherwise inedible grass by regurgitating it into their mouths, chewing it for a bit, and then swallowing it again – over and over again!

Snot

Snot is a defensive function, stopping for example germs, dirt and pollen before they get can get to your lungs.

The average person produces about 240 ml (½ pint) of snot per day. When you sneeze, up to about 3 L (6 pints) of air is blasted out of your lungs at up to 161 km/h (100 mph), along with any germs you may be carrying at the time. Sneezing is the main way that illnesses like colds and flu are spread among humans.

FACT

Emetophobia is the fear of vomiting or of being around others who are vomiting. It is the fifth most common phobia according to the International Emetophobia Society.

FACT

According to the World Toilet Organisation (no, really), the average person visits the toilet about 6–8 times a day, or 2,500 times a year, and spends three years of his or her life sitting on the toilet.

Feces

If you add up the time spent eating and drinking by an average person over the course of their whole life, it comes to 5 years. This adds up to 33 tons of food, which is equivalent to eating six entire elephants.

What goes in must come out. (Well, some of it. Most of that mass is water that you lose through sweating, breathing and peeing, or carbon that you breathe out in the form of carbon dioxide, while a lot of the rest goes into making new bits of your body to replace old bits.) The result is that during your lifetime you will produce a pile of poo about the size of a car.

Feces spread disease, which is why we have evolved to find the smell of poo revolting. But lots of animals seem to think it's a delicacy. Animals that eat poo include rats, mice, rabbits, dung beetles, flies, gorillas and dogs. Dogs are particularly fond of cat poo.

Flatulence

The average person produces about 0.5 L (1 pint) of flatus (the technical term for fart gas) per day, which is released in an average of 14 farts a day. Anyone who says they don't fart is lying or perhaps only does it while asleep and not aware of it.

Fabulous foodstuffs

Different cultures tend to have different attitudes to food and ideas about what constitutes a mouth-watering meal.

Food	Where	How it is prepared
Maggot cheese	Sardinia	Cheese is left out and flies deposit their eggs on it. The maggots hatch out and burrow through the cheese. When they are fat and plump the islanders eat the cheese, maggots and all. This is called carzu marzu – 'maggot cheese'.
Locusts	China, Sahara, Vietnam, Thailand	The Hani people of China's Yunnan Province offer deep-fried locusts and cooked chicken heads to important guests. In the Sahara, the Taureg people grind locusts down to make 'flour'. In Vietnam they are made into pancakes. In Thailand they eat battered 'grasshopper fritters'. Canned fried locusts have even been introduced as exotic bar snacks in New York – but in most other the western cities in the United States and in Europe they are greeted with revulsion.
Ants	Thailand	Ants are acidic and replace lemon in salads.
Water bugs	Thailand	The female water bug looks like a cockroach and is soaked in soy sauce to create a local delicacy. Water bug gourmets break off the head and legs, place the abdomen between the teeth, and squeeze the marinated 'meat' into the mouth.
Crickets	Nigeria, Thailand	In Nigeria crickets are roasted over a fire, then the guts are removed before eating. The Thai Farmers Research Centre has discovered that a cricket provides significantly more protein than traditional meats. A cricket is one-fifth protein: 100 g of cricket yields 20.6 g of protein, while the corresponding figure for beef is 18.8 g, pork 14.1 g, chicken 20.2 g and chicken eggs 12.7 g.

People around the world happily bite into foodstuffs you probably think are disgusting. Particularly popular are insects and reptiles.

Food	Where	How it is prepared
Winged termites or sausage flies	Ghana, South Africa	These insects are fried or roasted, or made into bread. In South Africa they are eaten with cornmeal porridge.
Aquatic fly larvae	Japan	Japanese gourmets favour aquatic fly larvae sautéed in soy and sugar.
Dragonflies	Bali	Dragonflies are boiled in coconut milk with ginger and garlic.
Tarantulas	Central America	Roasted.
Rattlesnakes	Texas, United States	In March each year, the citizens of Sweetwater, Texas, hunt down every living rattlesnake in what is claimed to be the world's largest rattlesnake roundup. The unfortunate snakes are killed, skinned and have their entrails removed before being cut into manageable slices and fried in batter.
Iguana	Mexico	In Mexico's Yucatan Peninsula, the locals enjoy 'iguana tacos', made from Gallina de Palo, meaning 'tree chickens', These large lizards, up to 1.2 m (4 ft) long, are caught in the forest and even in backyards. It's their tail meat that is prized.
Alligator	Louisiana, United States	In southern Louisiana, alligator kebabs are popular. They consist of slices of alligator tail meat covered with cornmeal batter.
Snake	Hong Kong	'Snake wine' is made from the contents of a snake's gall bladder. Elsewhere in China, snake wine is actually a 'wine', but with a small snake in the bottle.

Diseases

The deadliest creatures on Earth are the microscopic ones that cause diseases. They are effectively parasites, in that they use the human body to provide resources so that they can multiply and spread (disease is a side-effect of their growth, caused by depleting the body's nutrients, releasing toxins or damaging cells in order to get in or out of them). The most highly evolved ones are those that are least fatal, such as the common cold, because in general it makes little evolutionary sense to kill the host that feeds you.

Top five nastiest human diseases

This list is not official, but does reflect some of the horrible things that can happen to people – especially in the tropics.

1. **Hemorrhagic fever:** *Disease organisms such as the Ebola virus, Marburg virus and hantaviruses all cause a horrible disease where vague early symptoms of fever, joint pain and fatigue progress to severe bleeding all over and throughout the body, so that blood comes out of every orifice, such as the eyes and genitals. Eventually your organs break down and your system simply collapses. Some of these viruses have an incredibly high death rate, such as the Ebola-Zaire subtype of Ebola, which kills up to 90 per cent of those who become clinically ill.*

2. **Necrotising fasciitis:** *Known as the 'flesh-eating bacteria', this is a disease caused by usually fairly harmless bacteria, that get into soft tissues under the skin where they grow quickly and release toxins that eat away at the flesh. It can spread very quickly, and is able to destroy fist-sized chunks of organs and flesh in days .The main treatment is to cut out the infected flesh, so sufferers often require amputation or worse. Even with treatment a quarter of affected people die.*

3. **Smallpox:** *Fortunately eradicated from the human population (but still kept in some laboratories), the smallpox virus causes pustules (fluid-filled blisters) to break out over the entire surface of the body. These can join up so that the whole of your skin is one giant blister, at which point death is almost certain.*

4. **Hydatid disease:** *Also known as Echinococcosis, this is a parasitic infection where tapeworm eggs get into the body through the gut and latch onto the kidney, lungs, the liver, where they form cysts – balls full of thousands of tapeworm larvae. These can grow as big as a football. When they burst, death is almost inevitable.*

5. **Depression:** *This may not sound as nasty as the others, but severe depression is often fatal because it leads to suicide – in other words, it is so awful that people want to kill themselves. Imagine feeling like everything is utterly hopeless all the time and that you are completely worthless and rotten – this is what severe depression can be like.*

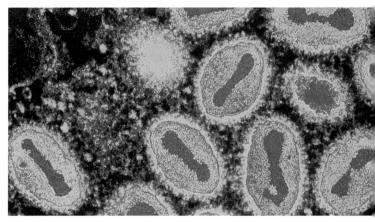

ABOVE Small pox virus; by 1980 the disease was eradicated by vaccination.

FACT

As if ordinary smallpox weren't bad enough, there is also another, even worse form of the disease, where instead of causing blistering of the skin it causes bleeding under the entire skin, so that the whole body turns black, including the eyes. The organs and the inside of the body also start to bleed, as in hemorrhagic fever. Death is guaranteed.

Sleeping and dreaming

On average humans need about six to eight hours of sleep a night, although everyone is different and the amount you need changes slightly throughout life.

The longest recorded time anyone has ever gone without sleeping was an American high school student named Randy Gardner, who, for a science fair project, stayed awake for 264 hours (11 days). However, for much of this period he was in an altered state of consciousness that was not really the same as being awake.

Time spent sleeping varies widely in the animal world, but generally the larger the animal the less time it needs to sleep. Giraffes sleep for about two hours a day, while bats can spend 20 hours a day sleeping. A marine mammal needs to stay awake to breathe, so only one half of its brain goes to sleep at a time.

Weird dreams

Except for some people with brain damage, everyone dreams, although not everyone can remember dreaming. On average you spend about two hours a night dreaming, which works out at six years spent dreaming during a typical lifespan. Most dreams last for between 5 and 20 minutes, which means you have, on average, between 6 and 24 dreams night.

FACT

Sleepwalking, known as somnambulism, affects around 18 per cent of the world's population. People are capable of doing all sorts of things while in their sleep, including eating bathing, and dressing. Some subjects have even been recorded driving cars and committing murder while are technically asleep.

Dream symbolism

Ever wondered what your dreams actually meant? Below are some common dream themes and their meanings

Dream symbol	What it means
Teeth	If the teeth are falling out, it usually means that the dreamer has difficulties getting his or her voice heard or feelings acknowledged.
House	Symbolises a larger aspect of your self. Different rooms in the house can represents various aspects, for example the bedroom can represent the unconscious mind aspect of the self.
Flying	Represents freedom from the physical body as well as a desire for freedom and escape from restraints.
School	Dreams about school relate to your current 'lesson in life'. Recurring dreams about school mean that you haven't learned your lesson yet!
Car/vehicle	Symbolises the physical body. Some of the details can be important: for example if you are the driver, this means that you are in control of your life; and if you are a passenger it might indicate that someone else is trying to take over your life.
Blood	Bleeding represents losing your energy and life force. The hurt can even be self-afflicted.
Telephone	This is a 'message' symbol, so it is important to note who is calling, what is being said, and if there are any difficulties with the phone.
Tornado	Represents inner turmoil – a 'whirlwind of emotions'. It is a sign to deal more effectively with your emotions and take control.
Being naked	Suggests a feeling of exposure and/or vulnerability.
Water	Often representing the 'sea of life', especially when water in the form of an ocean. Water also represents emotional turmoil.

Altered states of consciousness

Sleep and dreaming are probably the two most common altered states of consciousness, but there are many others, some of which are so common that almost everyone has experienced them at one time or another. There are ten most common naturally-occurring (i.e. not requiring drugs, fasting, sleep-deprivation, etc) states.

◆ **Time-gap experience:** *People driving long distances, or engaged in other absorbing but monotonous tasks, often report 'coming to' after some time and realising that time has passed without them being aware of it. This is a form of altered consciousness characterised by lack of awareness of time and surroundings, a sort of 'auto-pilot' mode.*

◆ **Deja-vu:** *The sensation of having seen, heard or experienced a new situation previously, can be characterised as a transient state of altered consciousness.*

◆ **Lucid dreaming:** *Conscious perception that one is dreaming. Dreamers are aware that they are dreaming and may even be able to direct or control the dream.*

◆ **Hypnosis:** *Some types of hypnosis for some subjects can cause an altered state usually characterised by relaxation, drowsiness or trance and high suggestibility.*

◆ **Migraine aura:** *Migraine sufferers often experience a phase of neurological symptoms heralding the onset of pain, characterised by hallucinations, including being able to see an aura around people and objects.*

◆ **Hypnagogia:** *An altered state experienced while falling asleep. Characterised by vivid and bizarre hallucinations in all senses, particularly a sensation of falling and a sensation of fear or a malevolent presence. Most of the population has or will experience this at least once in their lives; many people experience it regularly.*

◆ **Hypnopompia:** *Altered state experienced while waking up, that is similar to hypnogogia. Can be accompanied by sleep paralysis, where the mechanism that prevents dreamers from acting out their experiences* *persists, and the subject cannot move and often feels a crushing pressure on the chest.*

◆ **Out of body experience:** *A sensation of consciousness leaving the body, often with the ability to look back at it. 'Astral body' may be restricted to same room or may pass through walls and travel widely.*

◆ **Near-death experience:** *Probably caused by a lack of oxygen to the brain. Typically combines elements of out-of-body experience with life review (life flashing before the eyes), travel along a tunnel or towards a bright light, encounter with a presence or entities, encounter with deceased loved ones, sometimes even a tour of 'heaven'. On their return to normal conscious state, subjects typically feel their lives have new meaning and are changed by the experience.*

◆ **Temporal lobe epilepsy:** *Epilepsy is caused by random electrical activity in the brain ('brain-storms'). If these occur in the temporal lobe they may not cause physical symptoms (i.e. there are no convulsions), but they can cause altered consciousness, visions, hallucinations, presentiments, strange thoughts and paranormal experiences.*

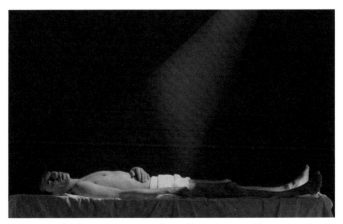

ABOVE Out of body experiences typically involve a sensation of floating outside of your body and, in some cases, seeing one's physical body from a place outside of the body (autoscopy). About one in ten people claim to have had an out-of-body experience at some time in their lives.

Unusual mutations

For many people suffering from debilitating disabilities or mutations that made it hard for them to fit into normal society. In the centuries gone by, exhibiting themselves for other people's amusement was the only way to make a living.

The Elephant Man

The Elephant Man is one of the best known examples of a human suffering from an unusual mutation. His real name was Joseph Merrick (1862–1890), a British man called the Elephant Man for his disfigured face and limbs. His deformity began developing at the age of five. In 1884, he took a job as a sideshow attraction and became something of a celebrity in Victorian high society.

He was originally believed to have elephantiasis (a parasitic disease) or neurofibromatosis (tumors on the nerves), but in 1986, it was suggested that Proteus syndrome closely fitted Merrick's symptoms. Proteus syndrome is a progressive genetic disorder, where children are born without symptoms but develop tissue and bone growths as they age. The severity and locations of these growths vary, but affected areas usually include the head, at least one limb and feet. There is no known cure for this disorder.

BELOW Historical artwork of Joseph Merrick, called the Elephant Man for his disfigured face and limbs.

Hairy people

A condition called congenital hypertrichosis causes hair to grow from every part of the skin, including the forehead, cheeks, nose and so on. If they let their hair grow, sufferers resemble a wolfman – both men and women. In times past people who had this condition became famous.

Petrus Gonzales: *The first recorded instance of this condition. Born in the Canary Islands in 1556, he became a celebrity at the court of King Henri II of France. He married a normal woman but had four hairy children.*

Barbara Urselin: *Born in Germany in 1629, Barbara Urselin was known as the Hairy Maid and entertained paying visitors all over the Europe by playing the harpsichord.*

The Sacred Hairy Family of Burma: *So-called by American showman P. T. Barnum in 1889, the family was a mother and son whose faces were covered with very long hair so that they looked like 'wookies' from the Star Wars movies.*

Jo-Jo the Dog-Faced Boy: *Possibly the best-known hairy person was Jo-Jo the Dog-Faced Boy, the stage name of Fedor Jefticheiev, a Russian man whose father had also been hairy all over. Poor Fedor was also exhibited by P. T. Barnum, and sometimes played the part of a dog for the gawking crowds. He spent at least 30 years being exhibited as a 'freak'.*

The family who walk on all fours

Discovered living in a Kurdish village in southeastern Turkey in 2005, five siblings of the Ulas family seem to be throwbacks to our quadrupedal ancestors – they walk on all fours. Their method of walking has been described as a 'bear crawl', because they walk on their palms, with their legs slightly bent at the knee, and their rears high in the air – unlike gorillas or chimpanzees, which walk on their knuckles. They can stand up for short periods with their knees bent. Scientists think the family present a unique insight into how early humans got about before bipedalism.

Strangest sideshow attractions

Today we frown upon the term 'freak', but before the Second World War the sideshow – a parade of anomalies, prodigies and freaks – was a popular form of entertainment. Within the sideshow there was a hierarchy, with 'Born Freaks' (those born with deformities or anomalies) at the top, 'Made Freaks' (people who had made themselves look like freaks through tattoos, body modification and so on) in the middle and 'Working Acts', such as fire-eaters and sword-swallowers, at the bottom. Some of the types of freak that could be found included:

- Albinos
- Bearded ladies
- Bug eyes (those who could pop their eyes out of their sockets at will)
- Deformed people (like, Joseph Merrick, the Elephant Man)
- Dwarves
- Extra limbs
- Geeks (people who ate live animals and acted mad, or sometimes were mad)
- Hairy people (see page 110-111)
- Hermaphrodites (people with both male and female sexual characteristics)
- Horned people (those with bony growths coming from the head or elsewhere)
- Hydrocephalic people (those with enormous skulls caused by fluid in the head)
- Living skeletons (those with extra-thin limbs or bodies)
- Lobster folk (those with hands split into two like lobster claws)
- Parasitic twins (partially formed conjoined twins)
- Penguin people (similar to turtle folk)
- Pinheads (smaller than usual skulls but normal-sized faces)
- Rubber-skins (those who could stretch their skin unnaturally)
- Seal folk (those with tiny, flipperlike arms)
- Siamese twins (today known as conjoined twins)
- Six-fingered and six-toed people
- Tailed folk
- Turtle folk (those with tiny forearms and hands/lower legs and feet, like a turtle or tortoises' limbs)

CURIOUS
CULTURES

Trends of human societies

Over the thousands of years that mankind has existed, different human societies and cultures have developed a whole array of bizarre and fascinating rituals and customs. From preserving the dead, to creating laws that defy all common sense, to suffering torture, execution, and some of the most unsuitable and tyrannical rulers you could possibly imagine controlling the course of history. If you think humans are weird individually, just wait until you see what we can get up to when we get together.

Amazing antiquity

The ancient Egyptians, Greeks and Romans are often thought of as the founders of civilisation, and it's true that in many ways they were a lot like us. In fact, a lot of the things we might assume were inventions of the modern world existed back in ancient times.

Oldest chewing gum

Archaeologists in Sweden found a 9,000-year-old piece of birch resin with teeth marks in it. The sticky, rubbery sap must have been chewed, making it the world's oldest ever chewing gum.

Artificial Egyptians

Prosthetics are artificial body parts made to replace real ones that have been lost through injury or disease. The discovery of a 3,000-year-old mummy with an artificial big toe, attached to the foot with linen strings, proves that the Egyptians had them long before us.

Hole in the head

'Trepanning' is the practice of drilling holes in the skull. It has legitimate medical value as it can relieve pressure on the brain from swelling caused by head injuries or internal bleeding. Amazingly, ancient skulls reveal that people were practicing highly professional medical trepanning 7,000 years ago, during the Stone Age.

Roman taxi

Taxis have literally been around since the year zero – a 2,000-year-old horse-drawn carriage that served as a taxicab has been dug up in Rome. Archaeologists know it was a taxi because it had an ingenious device for a meter – every time the rear wheel went round, a pebble would drop into a drum. The number of pebbles in the drum showed how far the carriage had travelled and determined the fare.

ABOVE 14th century engraving of trepanation, used to treat conditions such as migraines in the Middle Ages.

FACT

The ancient Chinese were the source of many inventions and technological advancements still in use today, including a system of writing, a calendar, gunpowder, printing, silk, paper and the compass.

How to make a mummy

The word "mummy" comes from the Arabic *mumiyah*, which means bitumen or pitch. (It was thought that tar was used to preserve the mummies, but in fact this was not the case.) Follow this simple recipe to make your own ancient-Egyptian-style mummy:

Ingredients

1 fresh corpse (ensure fully dead)
Hammer and chisel
Hook
Sharp knife
4 large jars
Several pints palm wine
Dozen blocks of salt from shores of Lake Wadi Natrun (a.k.a. 'natron'), wrapped in linen

100 g (4 oz) loose natron
Metal plate inscribed with Eye of Horus
Several metres fine linen bandages
Resin
Frankincense and myrrh
Magical amulets
Wooden and stone sarcophagi (coffins)

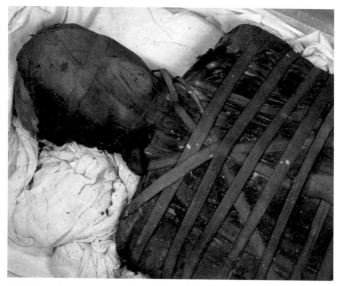

ABOVE Egyptian mummy, found in the Valley of the Mummies, in the Bahareya Oasis of the Western Desert, Egypt. The tombs date back to the 3rd century CE.

Method

1 Use a hammer and chisel to smash open nose of corpse and gain entry to skull.

2 Insert hook through this hole and wiggle around until brain is liquefied. Pour brain out of nose.

3 Make a small cut in the left-hand side of the abdomen; remove liver, stomach, kidneys, lungs and intestines. Leave heart in place. Place the removed organs in jars, and set aside for later.

4 Wash the body with palm wine to help sterilise it and prevent decay. If you can't find palm wine, vinegar will do.

5 Stuff the linen-wrapped blocks of natron salt into the empty body cavity to soak up water and help dry out the corpse. Cover outside of body with natron.

6 Leave for several days until fully dried out.

7 Brush off natron and seal up abdominal incision with inscribed metal plate.

8 Wrap body with linen bandages. For extra afterlife protection, write spells on the linen. Apply several wrappings.

9 Heat the resin with the frankincense and myrrh, and apply to bandages to seal in place. Repeat wrapping and resin application several times.

10 Decorate mummy with amulets.

11 Place mummy in a wooden sarcophagus and seal the lid shut. Then place this inside the stone sarcophagus. If particularly wealthy, use a lead sarcophagus between the wooden and stone ones.

12 Bury in rock-cut tomb decorated with elaborate murals and hieroglyphs. Surround with jars containing the removed organs, and various grave goods such as replica boats and containers made of precious metals. Leave to sit for 3,000–3,500 years, before rediscovering and displaying in museum. Curses optional.

FACT

During the Middle Ages, mummies became enormously popular as medicine. At first the resin-soaked bandages were thought to be health-giving, but eventually the whole mummy, bones, flesh, and all, was ground up and sold to people who would eat it!

Worst rulers in history

Unfortunately, having the top job is no guarantee of being able to do it. Here are 10 of the worst, most appallingly evil, or simply most wretched rulers in history.

Dates	Ruler	Offenses
12–41 CE	Caligula	Caligula is sometimes said to have been evil since infancy, but more usually thought to have been driven mad by an illness shortly after he became Emperor of Rome in 37 CE. He was accused of incest, torturing slaves for fun, selling the wives of senators as prostitutes, making his horse a senator, claiming to have won a war against the sea and tearing his own unborn child from his sister's womb. He insisted that he be worshipped as a god and had the heads of statues all over the Empire replaced with his own.
1368–1422	Charles VI the Mad of France	Afflicted with terrible fits of madness, Charles would attack people around him, forget his own name and wander his palaces howling like a wolf. He had delusions that he was made of glass and needed iron rods inserted into his clothing to keep him from breaking. He sometimes refused to wash for months until he was covered with lice. He once managed to set fire to a number of noble guests at a party (known as the Ball of the Burning Men), causing many deaths. He was responsible for many military disasters and a civil war.
1370–1419	Pope John XXIII	Known as an Antipope or false Pope (not to be confused with the genuine 20th-century Pope John XXIII), he bribed his way to power and was a notorious womaniser and degenerate. He ran prostitution and extortion rackets, and was later charged with piracy, murder, rape, sodomy, incest and even atheism.

Dates	Ruler	Offenses
1530–84	Ivan the Terrible	The most bloodthirsty ruler in Russian history until Stalin, Ivan earned his nickname for a reign of terror, with horrible torture methods and executions, such as boiling alive and being fed to starving dogs and bears. One area of the country was terrorised by secret police, who murdered whole families and on one occasion massacred the entire population of a city. He also beat his own son to death.
1889–1945	Adolf Hitler	Universally reviled as the most evil man in history, Hitler was responsible for a world war and a holocaust that involved the horrific industrial genocide of 10 million people. Millions more were forced into slave labour. When the war was clearly lost he refused to alleviate the suffering of the Germans and insisted that everyone should fight to the death.
1878–1953	Josef Stalin	A paranoid psychotic who inflicted purges, multiple genocides, and famine on the Russians, killing at least 10 million, but possibly twice that number.
1925–98	Pol Pot	Leader of the Khmer Rouge regime that ruled Cambodia from 1975–79. He oversaw a crazed attempt to destroy urban and modern life and return his country to the Middle Ages, which cost the lives of at least 1.5 million Cambodians.
1941–	Kim Jung-Il	Current leader of North Korea, the world's most tightly controlled state, with almost no political, press, or personal freedom. Almost the entire nation suffers from malnutrition because his backward policies leave the country unable to feed itself. Meanwhile Kim Jung-Il has fresh lobster airlifted to him daily so he can eat it with silver chopsticks.
1940–2006	Saparmurat Niyazov	Deranged dictator of Turkmenistan. He declared that any criticism of his policies was treason, and the only way to get to heaven was to read a book he had written. Regularly came out with absurd new laws, such as forbidding lip-synching and the playing of recorded music at weddings. Closed all the hospitals outside the capital and decreed that a huge ice palace be built in the middle of the desert.

Medieval Torturers

In Medieval times evidence obtained through torture was allowed in court; indeed, sometimes evidence was regarded as untrustworthy if it had not been obtained by torture. One result was a proliferation of ways to torture people, many of which concentrated on the feet, hands or fingers, as these could be tortured indefinitely without killing the prisoner.

Some medieval methods of torture

Type of torture	What it meant
Bastinado	Beating the soles of the feet with a stick or bar.
Waterboarding	Victim tied to a plank or board and plunged headfirst into water until nearly drowned.
Water cure	Victim's nostrils clamped shut and funnel forced down throat. Victim then forced to swallow large quantities of water or nastier fluid. The stomach becomes over-filled, causing great pain and vomiting, after which torture is repeated.
Denailing	Finger- or toenails ripped off. German witch-hunters would first use rough wooden skewers tipped in sulfur, which they would force under the nails to detach them from the nailbed.
Foot-roasting	Victim immobilised in stocks or frame and his bare soles, coated in lard or oil, are roasted over an open fire. As the torture progressed the foot would cook and split and bits of flesh and bone would fall off.
Mancuerda	A rope or cord is wound around the arms of the victim and then extreme pressure is applied to other end of cord, so that the victim is stretched as if on a rack and the cord cuts through the flesh of the arms.
Pitch-capping	Boiling hot pitch (tar) is poured into a bowl or cap, which is then upended onto the head of the bound victim. This boils the scalp. When the cap is ripped off it brings the scalp with it.

Inventive executioners

Throughout history people have thought up extraordinary ways to finish off criminals.

Asphyxiation
Beheading
Burning at the stake
Brazen bull (a hollow bull made of bronze, in which prisoners would be roasted to death)
Breaking on the wheel (tied to a wheel and having limbs repeatedly smashed with a hammer, then left to die a slow death)
Boiling to death
Burial alive
Crucifixion
Crushing by an elephant
Crushing by weight
Death-by-a-thousand-cuts
Devouring by animals
Disembowelment
Dismemberment
Drowning

Electrocution
Exsanguination (bled to death)
Forced suicide
Flaying (skinning)
Garroting (strangling with a wire)
Gassing
Guillotining
Hanging, drawing and quartering (dragged on a wooden frame, hanged for a short time by the neck, disembowelled and entrails burnt, beheaded and body divided into four parts)
Impalement
Lethal injection
Poisoning
Poisonous bites from animals
Starvation
Stoning
Tearing apart by horses
Trampling by horses

✳ FACT

The Knights Templar were an order of knights who were accused of all sorts of terrible crimes in the early 14th century. To gather evidence against them many were tortured, and foot-roasting was a favourite method of the inquisitors. One knight resisted for so long, and was so brave under torture, that he was later presented with a bag containing the bones from his feet that had fallen out during the roasting.

Fashion frenzy

Every generation has its bizarre fashion trends, with 'new looks' and 'the latest thing', but in truth there is little that is new under the sun. History offers many weird, amusing, unpleasant, or simply incredible trends, fashions and habits.

The codpiece

A piece of cloth to cover the 'cod', or genitals, was necessary in menswear of the late Middle Ages because men's hose (leg coverings) were either open at the crotch or too tight and constricting, while fashion dictated that the hemlines of doublets (tunics/jackets) rose steadily. In order to cover a gentleman's dignity, the codpiece (also known as a braguette) was introduced. At first it was just a flap of cloth, but later it was stylised into a padded, shaped appendage, which could double as a purse for carrying coins and snuff. The codpiece of Henry VIII may have been stuffed with anti-syphilitic medication to provide continuous treatment.

Penis gourds

Men of some tribes in New Guinea wear gourds (dried hollow fruits) to cover their genitals. These penis gourds were also known as phallocrypts, phallocarps, penis sheaths, *koteka* and *horim*. Typically the gourd is attached by twine around the base of the testicles and another around the waist. The size, design and angle of the gourd reflect tribal

> **FACT**
> No pain, no gain – in their quest for an hour-glass figure, some Victorian women wore their corsets so tight that they suffered broken ribs.

identity. Sometimes the gourds have secondary functions – double gourds have a space between them used for carrying money or tobacco, much like the codpiece of yore. Because of attempts by central government to suppress the wearing of *koteka*, it can now be a political act to sport one.

Neck-stretching

Tribes in Africa and southeast Asia practice a form of body modification involving the use of brass rings. From a young age they start to wear brass rings or coils of brass cable around the neck, gradually increasing the number so that over time their necks appear to be elongated like that of a giraffe. Medical authorities argue that what is actually happening is that the weight and pressure of the rings is deforming the collar-bones and other bones of the chest, compressing them so that the neck only appears longer.

Burqa

Islamic scriptures require women to dress modestly, interpreted by some Muslims to mean that women who might be seen by men outside the family, must cover up entirely. In Afghanistan such a covering takes the form of the burqa, a dress that covers the entire body from head to toe, with a grille or screen of gauze covering the slit for the eyes.

RIGHT Padaung tribal woman with many neck rings, Burma.

Pale skin

In most cultures visible signifiers of wealth and status are highly valued. In some cultures one such signifier is skin colour, which can relate to your leisure time and how much work you have to do. In pre-industrial times the poor had to toil in the fields, exposed to the sun, while the rich and powerful could stay indoors; hence pale skin signified high status. In order to enhance their pallor, women would employ a range of treatments and cosmetics, including chalk, powdered lead, lead oxide and even drinking vinegar. Unfortunately, lead-based cosmetics are toxic and probably caused significant mental problems.

Shocking shoes

Today many women's shoes have sharp pointed tips, but in the past it was men who sported absurdly pointy shoes. In the Middle Ages shoes called crackows or poulaines could have toes up to 64 cm (24 inches) long, stiffened with whalebone struts and stuffing. High heels were also popular with the men of yore, particularly in 17th century France during the reign of Louis XIV, who wore heels to compensate for his short stature. Perhaps the least comfortable footwear of all time was that worn by Chinese women who were subjected to foot-binding. The feet of young girls were tightly bound with cloth so that the bones would break and compress, leading to a small, squashed foot shape thought to resemble the lotus flower.

Merkins

A merkin is a pubic wig, traditionally worn to cover up places where pubic hair had been shaved because of lice, or to cover the marks of syphilis. They were often worn by prostitutes. The renewed popularity of burlesque is creating a demand for highly decorative merkins.

Strangest laws in the world

Many peculiar laws are the result of the failure to remove old legislation from the statute book, but some are simply the result of idiotic lawmakers.

Where	Law
Alaska	It is an offense to push a live moose out of a moving airplane.
New Jersey	It is illegal to wear a bulletproof vest while committing murder.
Marlboro, Massachusetts	It is an offense to detonate a nuclear device in the city.
Rhode Island	It is illegal to bite off another person's leg.
Louisiana	It is illegal to gargle in public places.
New Orleans	It is illegal for a woman to drive a car unless her husband is waving a flag in front of it.
France	It is illegal to name a pig Napoleon.
London, England	Taxicabs are required by law to carry a bale of hay and a sack of oats.
Georgia, United States	It is illegal to tie a giraffe to a telegraph pole.
Kentucky	Every citizen must take a bath at least once a year.
Oregon	It is illegal for bears to scrape the bark from plantation trees to get at the sap. The penalty for this misdemeanor is death.

Strange festivals and holidays of the world

People love to party, but some of the festivals and holidays celebrated around the world are simply peculiar.

Festival	Where	What happens
Vegetarian Festival	Phuket, Thailand	People follow a vegetarian diet to cleanse themselves, but more spectacularly, prove their piety and devotion by piercing their bodies with skewers, knives, swords, stakes – almost anything – as they march through the streets in a three-day procession.
Holi	India	People blow tubes of paint at one another and dump buckets of paint on the heads of passers-by, while laughing hysterically.
Mighty Mud Mania	Scottsdale, Arizona	Kids are encouraged to roll in and throw some 109,000 kg (240,000 lbs) of mud.
La Tomatina	Bunol, Spain	To celebrate the tomato harvest, the town stages the world's largest tomato fight.
Battaglia delle Arance (Battle of Oranges)	Ivrea, Italy	Staged to recreate a historical rebellion, this carnival involves a massive orange fight in which people who are not wearing a red cap are targets for everyone else.
Cheese rolling	Cooper's Hill, Gloucestershire, England	Contestants compete to see who can beat a large round cheese to the bottom of an incredibly steep hill. The course is only 275 m (900 ft) long but has a gradient of one in two. It is almost impossible to keep your feet and a high number of contestants end up with sprains or broken limbs.
Pandemonious Potted Pork Festival	Austin, Texas	A festival to celebrate SPAM (canned pork), with SPAM cook-offs, a SPAM-eating contest, SPAM throwing and a tug-of-war over a pit filled with SPAM jelly.

FREAKY
FUTURE

World of the future

Mankind has always been obsessed with the future; the better world that lies ahead and the amazing inventions that are just around the corner, about to revolutionise the way we live and make everything so much easier. Of course some of the inventions that come our way are just plain bizarre. But among the many technological misses, there are still valiant efforts, struggling to deliver the inventions that mankind has been dreaming of, that science fiction has been promising us, for so many years. It can only be a matter of time before the flying car swoops off our TV screens and into our garages.

Bizarre inventions

Humans have an inventive spirit, and there are scores of wannabe inventors out there who are just convinced that they've come up with the most incredible invention of the decade, the one thing missing from everyone's lives. The result tends to be a lot of weird inventions.

◆ **Life Expectancy Watch:** *(US Patent Issued In 2002) This cheerful little invention counts backwards towards the date of your eventual demise. You programme the watch by answering a series of questions about your lifestyle such as exercise, eating habits, and alcohol and tobacco use. Your remaining time on this earth is conveniently displayed*

✳ FACT

Thomas Edison filed 1,093 patents, including those for the light bulb, electric railways and the movie camera. When he died in 1931, he held 34 patents for the telephone, 141 for batteries, 150 for the telegraph and 389 patents for electric light and power.

in years, months days, and hours and an audible alarm can be set to remind you of your impending doom, just in case you were going to forget.

◆ **Motorised Ice cream Cone:** *(US Patent Issued In 1999)* Years of expending valuable energy to eat your ice cream are finally over! Just push the handy on/off switch on the side of the cone and your ice cream will spin round and round, and all you have to do is stick out your tongue.

◆ **Motorcycle Airbag:** *(US Patent Issued In 1989)* This all-over body suit airbag (must-have fashion at its best) is designed to cushion the motorcyclist's fall in an accident. When forcefully ejected from the bike the suit swells with compressed gas until it covers head, arms, torso and legs, to give you a (relatively) soft landing.

◆ **Toilet Snorkel:** *(US Patent Issued In 1982)* In most fires, it's the smoke that will get you, and a source of fresh air can be a life saver. So here it is – a way to snake a snorkel through the zigs and zags of your toilet, so you can breath sewer air instead of smoke.

◆ **Pet Petter:** *(US Patent Issued In 1989)* Some pets can be overly demanding of our attention. If you don't have the time to constantly coddle your pet, the Pet Petter does. An electric eye spots your pet and signals the electronic motors to start swinging the petting arm tipped with a human-like hand.

◆ **Electro Fishing:** *(US Patent Issued In 1993)* Some consider fishing a hobby and a skill. But if you don't have the time or patience for the traditional methods of hooking a fish, now you can wade out into your favourite fishing spot and drop your electrode into the water, causing 1,000 volts of electricity to surge through your victims, and instead of the struggle to keep your fish on the line as he fights for freedom, your victim will float to the surface. Much easier. Might be a good idea to bear in mind that electricity and water are quite a dangerous combination.

Futuristic Foods

We haven't replaced our food with synthetic substances just yet, but there are plenty of strange innovations going on in the world of nutrition.

Food pills

The eradication of food in favour of nutritional substitutes is a popular fantasy of the future – whether in the form of energy bars, diet shakes or, that old favourite, food pills. The hassle of meals a thing of the past, all the nutrition and energy you need reduced to pill form. Like the proton pill, taken by Roger Ramjet, the lead character in the US cartoon series by the same name; a single proton pill gave him the strength of twenty atom bombs for a period of twenty seconds. Food pills haven't caught on yet in our modern world of convenience; maybe the idea of replacing the Sunday roast with a pill doesn't actually appeal all that much in reality.

FACT
The first vending machine was invented by Hero of Alexandria around 215 BCE. When a coin was dropped into a slot, its weight would pull a cork out of a spigot and the machine would dispense a trickle of water.

Food in space

The first modern incarnation of a similar substance to food pills was enjoyed by astronauts; in the early 1960s, NASA contacted several leading food conglomerates hoping to come up with new and innovative ways of feeding astronauts on long-duration space missions. The result was 'food powder' – a nutritionally complete meal of freeze-dried food that was rehydrated in space and consumed through straws. Orbiting the Earth in zero gravity, astronauts faced an unappetizing choice of bite-sized cubes covered with edible gelatin or a semi-liquid food purée squeezed out of a toothpaste-like tube.

Other weird food

Futuristic innovations have been introduced to at a restaurant called Moto in Chicago by Homaro Cantu, an executive chef. A modified Canon i560 inkjet printer prints flavoured images onto edible paper. The print cartridges are filled with food-based 'inks', including juiced carrots, tomatoes and purple potatoes, and the paper tray contains sheets of soybean and potato starch. The printouts are flavoured by dipping them in a powder of dehydrated soy sauce, squash, sugar, vegetables or sour cream and then they are frozen, baked or fried.

Creepy Candy

- *Toffee scorpion (don't worry, the sting has been removed)*
- *Tequila-flavoured worm-inside-a-lollipop*
- *Chocolate-covered crickets*
- *Fruit-flavoured Butterfly Candy (the wings are made from a flower but there's a real insect pupae in the middle)*
- *Edible ant farm, encased in candy*
- *BBQ-flavoured worms*

RIGHT Scorpion encased in candy for a tasty treat.

Things you can buy from vending machines

With one vending machine for 23 people, Japan has the highest density of vending machines per capita in the world. The first vending machine in Japan was made of wood and sold postage stamps and post cards. They are a lucrative business – figures from 1999 record the estimated 5.6 million coin- and card-operated Japanese vending machines generated US$53.28 billion in sales.

Vending machines don't just offer soft drinks and candy bars anymore; you can get hold of quite a remarkable range of products from vending machines around the world.

Some strange vending machines

Category	Products
Food & drink	Fresh farm eggs; fresh vegetables; fried foods; French fries; dumplings; hot dogs; live lobsters; ice cream; rice; dry ice; Liquor House Mini (a range of alcoholic drinks)
Technology	iPods; batteries; CDs and DVDs; blood pressure measurement service; refrigerated food storage lockers; cell telephone recharging service (the user locks their plugged telephone in place to charge while he or she shops)
Last-minute gifts and toys	Flowers; jewellery; postcards; balloons; Rhinoceros beetles (sold as children's pets); airsoft pistols
Forgotten necessities	Toilet paper; umbrellas; kerosene; fishing lines, fish hooks, fish bait
Sex shop	A selection of pornography; schoolgirls' underwear

Robots

The market for household robots that perform all the humdrum, time-consuming chores that no one else wants to do, like vacuuming and lawn mowing, is continually expanding. But while domestic helper robots are one of the most popular types around, other robots have far more interesting roles in the human world.

Space Exploration: *It is dangerous for humans to get to space, to be in space and to return from space. As well as exploration and gathering information, robots can perform vital roles in space station operation and maintenance significantly reducing astronaut Extravehicular Activities, (EVA) which is very dangerous due to exposure to radiation and the probability of collision with extraterrestrial objects.*

Underwater: *Robotic models are used for underwater missions and exploration as well. The physiological effects of water pressure limit how long commercial divers can stay underwater, but robotic submersibles can operate twenty-four hours a day, thousands of metres below the surface. They can be used for observation, geological coring, seismology, oceanographic surveying, analysis and sampling, and are used by oil companies to service offshore oil operation structures.*

Artificial intelligence: *The next step for robot technology is artificial intelligence; programmes that can successfully interact with humans and perform tasks autonomously, including programmes that can play games such as chess, programmes known as 'chatbots', with which a human can have a typed conversation (although if you spend any time with them you'll notice that they spout back gibberish to slightly complex questions) and even vehicles that can steer and navigate for themselves. The technology still has a long way to go before human intelligence is indistinguishable from artificial intelligence, so for the moment we'll just have to continue thinking for ourselves.*

Robot Pets

We may not have robots level with human intelligence yet, but we can have a robot pet. The low-cost robotic pets and companions available today are more like toys than replacements for their biological equivalents but there are companies investing heavily in consumer robot technology. Sony's robo-dog AIBO is the best-known effort to provide an affordable robotic companion, but it was an expensive toy for robot enthusiasts. Able to walk, 'see' its environment via camera, and recognise spoken commands, they are able to learn and mature based on external stimuli from their owner or environment, or from other AIBOs. Furby and Robosapien are some of the closest robotic companions on the market today. In terms of robotic pets, the Furby has probably been the most successful. The soft toy has expressive motorised eyes and a limited vocabulary that improves over time. So if you love animals, but hate litter boxes or are allergic to fur, an artificial pet might be the answer. You can programme it to behave exactly as you like, so you get the benefits of companionship without any of the side effects. And there's no need to worry about getting home on time to feed it or arranging for someone to look after it while you're on holiday – if it gets inconvenient or annoying, simply turn it off.

LEFT The Sony dog robot, AIBO 220.

Transport of the future

New and better forms of transport are one of the big
dreams of future technology, to make the long hours of
commuting and traffic jams a thing of the past, and holiday
travel an almost pleasurable experience. Science fiction has
come up with so may options, all we have to do is wait for
an inventor to actually bring them into reality.

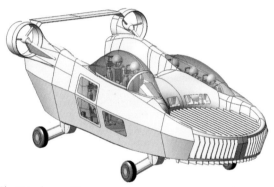

ABOVE The X-Hawk, one of the many attempts at creating a genuine flying car.

Flying Car

The flying car is probably the most sought-after transport of
the future. Mankind has been awaiting the flying car for a long
time – science fiction has been promising it since the 1960s
with George Jetson's Spacion Wagon, and it's made repeated
appearances since then: *Star Wars* (1977), *BladeRunner* (1982),
The Fifth Element (1997) to name a few.

More than 70 flying car patents have been filed with
the US Patent Office since the beginning of the 20th
century, but only a handful have ever been built and even
fewer have flown. In fact only two – the Amphibian and
the Aerocar – have actually been certified as both road-
and air-worthy.

Some attempted models of the flying car

There have been many attempts at fulfilling one of science fictions long-standing dreams, some of which have had more success than others.

Models of flying cars	How far did they get?
Curtiss Autoplane	Never really flew, but achieved a few short hops in 1917
Arrowbile	1937 had some success but was shelved in 1957 as there wasn't enough interest to make it successful
Saucer-shaped Avrocar,	A 'flying jeep' designed by the Canadian and British military to carry troops, abandoned in 1961 due to thrust and stability problems.
Aerocar	The most successful attempt was a fixed-wing plane-car hybrid. In the air, the Aerocar had a range of 800 km (500 miles) and a cruising speed of 217 km/h (135 mph). It first flew in 1949, but a business deal went sour in the 1960s, and it never went into production
The Moller M400 Skycar	A vertical takeoff and landing (VTOL) craft that inventor Paul Moller says will be available this decade in limited quantities, so keep an eye out!
X-Hawk	Another viable craft is a rotorless VTOL aircraft being built by Urban Aeronautics, which is being positioned as a flying vehicle for urban environments that could be used as medivac, taxi or patrol craft.
The Transition	Meanwhile Terrafugia, Inc. is developing a personal air vehicle that looks like an sport utility vehicle (SUV) with retractable wings.

Jetpack

Imagine strapping on a piece of jet-powered luggage and being able to fly anywhere you like. The jetpack is one of the most popular icons of sci-fi: just imagine the joyriding thrill (and ignore the potential mayhem of hundreds of jetpack-borne people hurtling through the skies!)

Sadly jetpacks aren't available in your local store just yet; the past 60 or 70 years haven't seen any great advances in this technology. Bell Aerosystem's original 'rocket belt' could propel its pilot into the air for about 20 seconds, and by the 1960s this had increased by only 10 seconds. A jetpack has a limited fuel capacity so more recent research has run into similar problems.

ABOVE Sean Connery as James Bond in *Thunderball* from 1965, sporting a jetpack.

CHAPTER SEVEN

How to work your jetpack (don't try this at home!)

1. *Two canisters mounted on the pilot's back are filled with about 27 litres (six gallons) of purified hydrogen peroxide.*

2. *The pilot releases a lever that causes pressurised nitrogen to push the propellant into a chamber, where it makes contact with a silver or copper catalyst.*

3. *Hydrogen peroxide decomposes naturally into water and oxygen in an heat-producing reaction. A catalyst like silver or copper speeds the reaction up, resulting in superheated steam and oxygen at a temperature of about 743ºC (1370ºF).*

4. *This gas mixture creates 140 kg (300 lb) of thrust as it blasts out of the nozzles at the base of the jetpack.*

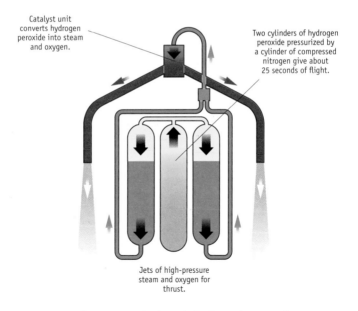

Catalyst unit converts hydrogen peroxide into steam and oxygen.

Two cylinders of hydrogen peroxide pressurized by a cylinder of compressed nitrogen give about 25 seconds of flight.

Jets of high-pressure steam and oxygen for thrust.

ABOVE Diagram demonstrating the theory behind a working jetpack.

Transporters

Transporters would get you from place to place without having to pass through the intervening space – imagine all the time wasted travelling that could be saved and the discomfort that could be spared.

If a functional teleporter was invented, the person or object wouldn't actually be physically moved it would work more like a computer scanner. The original would be scanned, the data about them transmitted and a precise copy would be made at the receiving end. Unfortunately the original would be destroyed. If that's a ham sandwich, that's one thing. Having a friend or family member cloned and destroyed might be a little harder to accept.

Unfortunately this technology hasn't advanced very far along just yet either, but science fiction hasn't given up on the idea: the scientist in the 1958 Vincent Price film *The Fly* (remade in 1986 and 2006) recombines his DNA with that of a fly in his attempts at teleportation; the characters of *Star Trek* characters have more success with their model; the 1994 film and subsequent TV series *Stargate* is based entirely on the premise of travelling to distant worlds through teleportation, and Douglas Adams includes the idea in his *Hitchhiker's Guide to the Galaxy* series, with the perhaps off-putting description of 'not quite as fun as a good solid kick to the head'.

FACT

The first (qualified) transporter success came in 1993, when a research team at IBM, led by Charles Bennet, confirmed that quantum teleportation is possible, but only if the original object or person is destroyed – which is a bit of a deterrent.

Page numbers in *italic* type refer to illustrations.

A

alchemy **18**
alien big cats **9**
aliens *see* extraterrestrials (ETs)
Antarctica **63**, **67**, **71**
Antipope **118**
appendix **95**
Aral Sea **71**
Area 51 **49**, *49*
Arica, Chile **60**
Arnold, Kenneth **53**
arthropods **86–7**
artificial intelligence **133**
asteroids **32**, *42*
astronauts **44**, **45**, **130–1**
Atacama Desert **63**
Atlantis **16**, *17*

B

bacteria **92**, **94**, **104**
Ball of Burning Men **118**
ball lightning **62**
banana slug **75**, *75*
bat **106**
    droppings **69**
bee **80**
Big Bang **34**, *35*
Bigfoot *8*, **9**
bile **94**
bilocation **29**
bitter taste **97**
black holes **37**
black projects **51**
blood **93**, **99**
    squirted **77**
blue jets **62**
bodily fluids **99–101**
bombardier beetle **87**
bones **94**
bonnacon **10**, *10*
box jellyfish **80**
brain **93**
bristlecone pine **79**

buffalo, Cape **81**
burning at the stake **22**, *22*
burqa **123**
burrowing owl **76**

C

Caligula **118**
carpet viper **80**
castor oil plant **88**
cells in human body **92**
    death and replacement **93**, **94**
Charles VI, the Mad of France **118**
cherubim **31**
chewing gum **114**
chimpanzee **90**
chupacabras **9**
clairvoyance **25**
Clever Hans the horse **89**
Close Encounters (CE) scale **50**
clothing **122–3**
cockroach **69**
codpiece **122**
coldest place **63**
colour vision **96**
coup de foudre **13**
crab, boxing glove (pom-pom) **87**, *87*
creation myths **31**, **32**
crocodile *81*, **82**
cryptozoology **9–10**
crystal ball **20**
crystal caves **70**, *70*
cyclones **58–9**

D

Danaïdes **30**
dangerous animals **79–85**
dark matter **35**
datura **88**
Dead Sea **67**, *67*
deadly nightshade **88**
death cap **88**, *88*
decibel levels and effects **98**
Deer Cave, Malaysia **69**
deja-vu **108**
demons **29**

diabetes **96**
dinosaurs **84–5**, *85*
diseases **104–5**
divination **18–20**
Doctrine of Correspondences **21**
dog **83**
dolphin **90**
dreams **105–6**, **108**
dysentery **80**

E

Earth **36**, **38–9**
    atmosphere **44**
    Extinction Level Events (ELEs)
        42–3
    orbital debris *44*
earthquakes **64–5**, **68**
ecological collapse **43**
ectoplasm **15**
Edison, Thomas **129**
ejaculation **94–5**
electric people **26–7**
electromagnetic pollution **43**
elephant **82**
Elephant Man **110**, *110*
emetophobia **100**
Enceladus **47**
epilepsy, temporal lobe **109**
Europa **47**, **71**
Evening Star **38**
Everest, Mount **67**
evil eye **18**
execution methods **121**
Extinction Level Events (ELEs) **42–3**
extra-sensory perception (ESP) **25**
extraterrestrials (ETs) **46–54**, **71**
    alien abductions **51**, **53**, **54**
eyes **96**

F

fairies, summoning **24**
fake tongue louse *76*, **77**
feaces **92**, **101**
festivals **126**
fierce snake **80**
fingernails **94**

fire walking **28**
fire winds **60**
flatulence **101**
flies **80**
flying car **135–6**, *135*
food **101**
    futuristic **130–1**
    strange foodstuffs **102–3**
foot-binding **124**
foxglove **88**
Frankenstein Effect **43**
fulmar **74**

G

gall bladder **95**, *95*
gamma-ray burst **43**
gecko **76**
ghosts **12**
giraffe **106**
gods and goddesses **31**
gorilla **90**
gravity **36–7**, **38**
grizzly bear **82**, **84**
Gulf Breeze **48**

H

Hades **30**
hagfish **75**
hailstone, biggest **64**, *64*
hair **94**, **111**
haunted house **12**
Hawaiian Trough **67**
hearing **97–8**
heart **93**, *93*
Hecantonchires **31**
Hessdale **48**
hippo **81**
Hitler, Adolf **119**
Hopkins, Matthew **23**
hottest place **63**
humans **43**, **80**, **92–112**
hurricanes **58–9**
Hyperborea **16**
hypertrichosis **111**
hypnagogia **108**
hypnopompia **108–9**

hypnosis **108**

I

ideomotor effect **15**
immune system **94**, **99**
inland taipan **80**
insects **86–7**
intelligent animals **89–90**
inventions, bizarre **128–31**
Ivan the Terrible **119**
Ixion **30**

J

jellyfish **80**
jetpack **137–8**, *137*
jimsonweed **88**
jumper, highest **86**
Jupiter **36**, *41*, **45**

K

Kabbalah **18**
Karman line **44**
Katrina, Hurricane **59**
kidney **94**
Kim Jung-Il **119**
King Kong **84–5**

L

lake monsters **9**
lakes **71**
Law of Association **21**
laws, strange **125**
Lechuguilla Cave **70**, *70*
Leidenfrost effect **28**
Lemuria **16**
levitation *15*, **29**
lightning **61–3**, *61*
lion **84**
liver **94**
Loch Ness Monster **9**
lost civilizations **16**, *17*

M

magic **18–24**
magnetic people **26–7**
malaria **80**

Marfa **48**
Mars **36**, **38–40**, *40*, **47**
Mauna Kea **67**
mediums **14–15**, *15*
Mercury **36**, **38–40**, *40*
merkin **124**
meteors *42*, **43**
Methuselah pine **79**
migraine aura **108**
Moodus noises **72**
Moon **36**, **38**, **45**, **47**
Morning Star **38**
mosquitoes **80**
mucus **74–5**, **99**
mummies **116–17**, *116*
mushrooms, poisonous **88**, *88*
mutations **110–12**
myths **30–2**

N

nanotechnology **43**
near-death experience **109**
neck-stretching **123**, *123*
necromancy **18**
Neptune **36**, **38–9**, **41**, *41*, **45**
neutron stars **35–6**
Niyazov, Saparmurat **119**
Nullabor Plain **48**

O

ocean quahog **79**
octopus **90**
    mimic **78**
oldest plants and animals **79**
Operation Stargate **26**
opossum **78**
ouija board **15**
out of body experience **109**

P

palms, reading **20**, *21*
pancreas *94*
parapsychology **25**, **26**
parasites *76*, **77**, **105**
parrot **90**
parrotfish **75**

penis gourd **122–3**
pillars of fire **60**
Pioneer II **45**
Pirithous **30**
plagues **43**
planets **36**, **38–41**, *40*, *41*
plasmodium **80**
Pluto **36**, **38–9**, **41**, *41*
poisons
    poisonous plants **88**, *88*
    venomous animals **80**
Pol Pot **119**
pollution **43**
Pope John XXIII **118**
potato beetle **88**
precognition **25**
prosthetics **114**
pubic wig **124**

R

rain **56–7**, **60**, **63**
red sprites **62**
Rendlesham Forest **53**
retina **96**
ribs **94**
ricin **88**
ringing rocks **72**
robots **133–4**, *134*
Roswell *52*, **53**
rulers, worst in history **118–19**

S

saints **29**
saliva **99**
salty taste **97**
Saturn **36**, **38–9**, **41**, *41*, **45**
scrying **20**
sea serpent **9**
sea wasp **80**
séance **14–15**
senses **96–8**
Shansi earthquake **68**
shark **83**
shoes **124**
shrimp
    mantis **86–7**, **90**

snapping (pistol) **86**
singing sands **72**
Sisyphus **30**
six-eyed sand spider **80**
skeleton **94**
skin **94**, **97**
    color **124**
skunk **77**
sleep **106**
slime **74–5**, *75*
slug **75**, *75*
smallpox **104**, **105**, *105*
smell, sense of **96**
snake, most venomous **80**
sneezing **100**
snot **100**
snow, coloured **58**
sour taste **97**
space **34–47**
space exploration **44–6**, **130–1**, **133**
space junk *44*, **45**
spells **24**
sperm **94–5**
spider **78**, *79*, **80**
spine **94**
spiritualism **14–15**
spittlebug **86**
spleen **94**
Stalin, Josef **119**
stars **35–6**, **37**
stigmata **29**
stonefish **80**
strange rains **56–7**
sweat **94**
sweet taste **97**

T

Tambora, Mount **68**
Tantalus **30**
tarantula **78**, *79*
taste, sense of **97**
taxis **115**
telekinensis **25**
telepathy **25**
teleportation **139**
temperature extremes **63**

Texas horned lizard **77**
thunder **61**
tiger **82**, **84**
time-gap experience **108**
Titan **47**
Tityus **30**
Toby the thinking pig **89**
toenails **94**
tornadoes **58–9**
tortoise **79**
torture **120–1**
touch, sense of **97**
transport, futuristic **135–9**
transporter **139**
trepanation **115**, *115*
trial by ordeal **23**
tsunamis **64–5**, *65*
tubeworm **79**
typhoons **58–9**
Tyrannosaurus rex **84–5**, *85*

U

umami taste **97**
unidentified flying objects (UFOs) **34**,
   48–54
   major sightings **53**
   UFO hotspots **48**
Universe **34–7**
Uranus **36**, **38–9**, **41**, *41*, **45**
urine **96**, **99**

V

vaccination **105**
Valentich Incident **53**

vampire **11–12**, **29**
vending machine **130**, **132**
venomous animals **80**
Venus **36**, **38–40**, *40*
vision **96**
Vlad the Impaler **11**
volcanoes **42**, **67**, **68**
vomit **100**
Vostok, Lake **71**
Voyager space probes **45**, **46**

W

Waialeale, Hawaii **60**
Warminster **48**
wasp **80**
waterguns **72**
waves **64–6**, *65*
weight **36**
werewolf **13**
wicca **18**
wind **58–60**
witch-finders **23**
witchcraft **18–24**
witches' marks **23**

X

X-ray vision **27**
Xena **38**

Z

zombie **13**

PICTURE CREDITS

The publishers would like to thank the following for permission to reproduce pictures.

Getty: pp. 8, 21 22, 28, 46, 49, 52, 110, 113, 134; iStockphoto: pp. 7, 33, 39, 54, 55, 60, 79, 90, 129, 131; Kobal: p. 137; NASA: pp. 34, 40, 41, 44; NOAA: pp. 58-59, 62, 64; Photolibrary: pp. 11, 100, 125; Richard Burgess: pp. 39, 65, 138; Science Photo Library: pp. 15, 42, 58, 61, 87, 91, 92, 93, 95, 105, 109, 116, 118